SCIENCE WORKSHOP SERIES
CHEMISTRY
Reactions

Seymour Rosen

GLOBE BOOK COMPANY
A Division of Simon & Schuster
Englewood Cliffs, New Jersey

THE AUTHOR

Seymour Rosen received his B.A. and M.S. degrees from Brooklyn College. He taught science in the New York City School System for twenty-seven years. Mr. Rosen was also a contributing participant in a teacher-training program for the development of science curriculum for the New York City Board of Education.

Cover Photograph: Larry Lee/Westlight
Photo Researcher: Rhoda Sidney

Photo Credits:

P. 20, Fig. C: Abe Rezny/The Image Works
p. 36: P. Plailly/SPL/Photo Researchers
p. 41, Fig. H: Reynolds Metal Company
p. 41, Fig. I: UPI/Bettmann Newsphotos
p. 41, Fig. J: U.S. Steel
p. 58, Fig. A: Helena Frost
p. 84, Fig. I: U.S. Department of Energy
p. 105, Fig. A: Helena Frost
p. 105, Fig. B: Helena Frost
p. 110: Courtesy of General Electric
p. 113, Fig. A: Helena Frost
p. 113, Fig. B: UPI/Bettmann Newsphotos
p. 113, Fig. C: UPI/Bettmann Newsphotos
p. 116, Fig. E: Mark Antman/The Image Works
p. 120, Fig. C: Ray Ellis/Photo Researchers
p. 144: Rhoda Sidney
p. 147, Fig. A: Helena Frost
p. 147, Fig. B: New York Convention and Visitors Bureau
p. 149, Fig. E: The Port Authority of New York and New Jersey
p. 149, Fig. F: Helena Frost
p. 149, Fig. G: Helena Frost

ISBN: 0-8359-0340-0

Printed in the United States of America
    4 5 6 7 8 9 10   95

 Globe Book Company
A Division of Simon & Schuster
Englewood Cliffs, New Jersey

CONTENTS

METALS

Introduction to Reactions

Workers scrape and paint a rusty handrail on an apartment building. Factory workers put a shiny chrome coat on a piece of steel. A wood log burns in a fireplace.

What do these events have in common? They all involve chemical reactions. Chemical reactions affect every part of your life, right down to the food you eat and the clothes you wear.

Take ordinary table salt, for instance. You probably eat some every day. It is made up of two substances, sodium and chlorine. Did you know that sodium is a metal that, when in pure form, burns violently in water? Did you know that chlorine in its pure form is a toxic and dangerous gas? Yet combined as table salt, sodium and chlorine are quite safe.

This book will teach you about simple chemical reactions involving elements and compounds. After you have explored some basic ideas about the building blocks of matter, you'll learn how metals and nonmetals react to form materials you see everyday. You'll also discover the special properties of metals, and how they affect your life.

What is matter made of? | 1

atoms: the smallest parts of an element that have all the properties of that element
compound: matter made up of two or more elements that are linked together
element: matter that is made up of only one kind of atom
mass: a measure of the amount of matter
matter: anything that has mass and volume
volume: the amount of space that matter takes up

LESSON 1 | What is matter made of?

Matter is all around you. This book is matter. Water is matter. So is air. You are matter. In fact, everything you can see, and most of what you cannot see, is matter.

Matter is anything that has **mass** and **volume.**

Matter comes in three forms, called <u>states of matter</u>. The three states are solid, liquid, and gas.

All matter is made up of **atoms**, which are called the building blocks of matter. Atoms are unbelievably small. They're much too small to be seen with a microscope. The period at the end of this sentence has more atoms than you could count in a lifetime.

The total number of atoms in the world is impossible to count. But the different kinds of atoms known are limited in number. In fact, there are only 109 different kinds of atoms that have been found by scientists.

Some matter is made up of only one kind of atom. Most matter, however, is made up of two or more different kinds of atoms linked together.

Matter made up of only one kind of atom is called an **element.** There are 109 kinds of elements. That's one element for each different kind of atom. You know the names of many elements. Oxygen, iron, gold, silver, and aluminum are elements. How many other elements can you name?

Matter made up of two or more different kinds of atoms linked together is called a **compound.** There are millions of different compounds. That's because there are many different ways to link different kinds of atoms together. Almost everything you see around you is made of compounds. Water and salt are compounds. Wood, plastic, the paper and ink in this book, and even your own flesh and blood, are made of compounds.

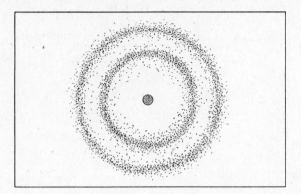

Figure A

Look at the figures. Then answer the questions.

Figure A shows a model of what scientists think an atom looks like.

Different elements have different atoms. The atoms of any one element are almost exactly alike. But they are different from the atoms of all other elements.

1. What is all matter made of? _____

2. Does matter have mass and volume? _____

3. Do atoms have mass and volume? _____

4. How many different kinds of atoms are there? _____

5. What do we call matter made up of only one kind of atom? _____

6. How many elements are there? _____

7. Name three elements. _____ _____ _____

8. The smallest part of an element is _____ atom of that element.
   just one, more than one

Figure B *Most types of matter exist as compounds.*

Most matter is made up of two or more different kinds of atoms linked together.

9. What do we call matter made of different kinds of atoms linked together?

   _____

10. There are _____
    more, fewer

    elements than there are compounds.

11. Name three compounds.

    _____ _____

    _____

12. Does a compound have mass and

    volume? _____

The smallest part of a compound is called a <u>molecule</u>.

Figure C shows a model of one molecule of water.

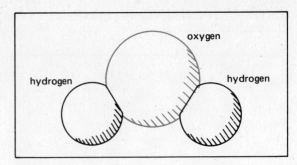

Figure C

13. How many different kinds of atoms make up a molecule of water? _____

14. Name the kinds of atoms that make up a water molecule. _____

    _____

15. How many atoms of hydrogen does one molecule of water have? _____

16. How many atoms of oxygen does one molecule of water have? _____

17. Altogether, how many atoms does one molecule of water have? _____

18. The smallest part of a compound is _____ molecule of that compound.
    <small>just one, more than one</small>

USING SYMBOLS

The shorthand way of writing an element's name is called its <u>symbol</u>. The symbols of all the elements are listed in the table on pages 166-167. (You will learn more about this table in Lesson 3.)

Use the table to help you write the names of elements whose symbols are shown below.

1. O _____   2. Li _____   3. Cl _____

4. Na _____   5. H _____   6. Fe _____

7. S _____   8. C _____   9. Ca _____

The shorthand way of writing a compound's name is called its <u>formula</u>. A formula is written using the symbols of the elements that make up a compound. The formula for the compound water, for example, is H_2O (see Figure C). In water, two atoms of hydrogen are linked to one atom of oxygen.

Five formulas are listed in the chart below. What are their chemical names? Choose from the following:

magnesium oxide	copper sulfate	carbon dioxide
silver iodide	sodium chloride	

Write each name next to the correct formula. (Hint: First use pages 166-167 to find out what each symbol stands for.)

	Formula	Chemical Name
10.	CO_2	
11.	NaCl	
12.	MgO	
13.	AgI	
14.	$CuSO_4$	

Figure D shows one molecule of a compound you know.

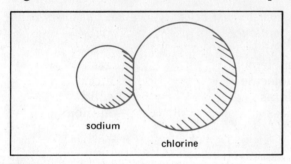

Figure D *The formula for this compound is NaCl.*

15. How many atoms make up one molecule of NaCl? _____

16. Name the elements that make up NaCl. _____

_____

17. Take a guess. What is the common name of this compound? (Hint: You put in on food.) _____

Figure E shows one molecule of a compound called sodium bicarbonate. You know it as baking soda.

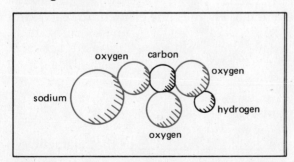

Figure E *The formula for baking soda is $NaHCO_3$.*

18. Name the four kinds of atoms in baking soda. _____

_____ _____

_____

19. How many atoms make up one molecule of this compound?

_____

A SWEET STORY

1. The formula for table sugar is $C_{12}H_{22}O_{11}$. Sugar is _____ .
    <small>an element, a compound</small>

2. How many different kinds of atoms does sugar have? _____

3. Name the elements that make up sugar. _____   _____

    _____

4. One molecule of sugar has   a)   _____ atoms of carbon.

    b)   _____ atoms of hydrogen, and

    c)   _____ atoms of oxygen.

5. Altogether, how many atoms does one molecule of table sugar have? _____

FILL IN THE BLANK

Complete each statement using a term or terms from the list below. Write your answers in the spaces provided. Some words may be used more than once.

liquid	an element	gas
a compound	molecule	atom
109	atoms	solid
volume	mass	millions

1. Matter has _____ and _____ .

2. The three states of matter are _____ , _____ , and

    _____ .

3. All matter is made up of _____ .

4. Matter that has only one kind of atom is called _____ .

5. There are _____ different elements. There is one element for each kind

    of _____ .

6. Linked-up atoms form matter called _____ .

7. There are _____ of compounds.

8. The smallest part of an element is just one _____ of that element.

9. The smallest part of a compound is just one _____ of that compound.

What parts make up an atom?

2

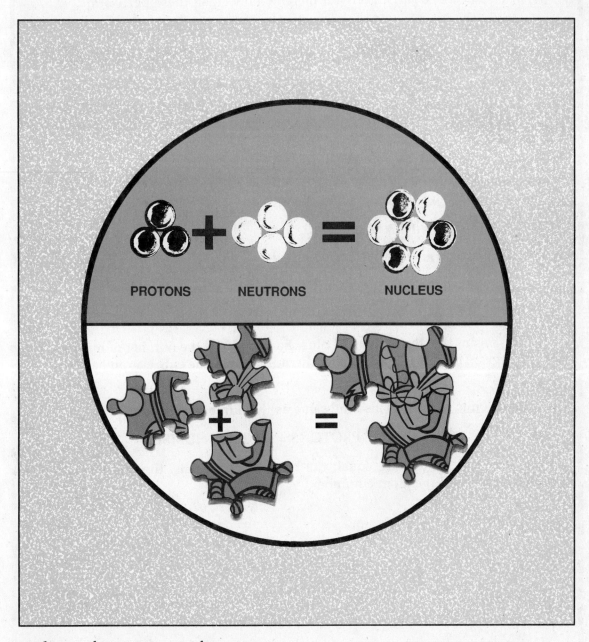

PROTONS   NEUTRONS   NUCLEUS

nucleus: the center part of an atom
proton: a part of the atom found inside the nucleus; a proton has a positive electrical charge
neutron: a part of the atom found inside the nucleus; a neutron has no electrical charge
electron: a part of the atom that moves around the nucleus; an electron has a negative electrical charge

LESSON 2 | What parts make up an atom?

It is hard to believe how tiny an atom is. Yet, the tiny atom is made up of even smaller parts. Can you imagine how small these parts are?

An atom has three main parts: **protons**, **neutrons**, and **electrons**.

Protons and neutrons make up the center of an atom. The center of an atom is called the **nucleus**.

The electrons are outside the nucleus. They spin around the nucleus at very great speeds. Electrons have much less mass than protons or neutrons.

Protons and electrons have electrical charges.

- Each proton has a <u>positive</u> (+) charge.

- Each electron has a <u>negative</u> (–) charge.

- A neutron is neutral. It has no charge.

An atom has the same number of protons as electrons.

NUMBER OF PROTONS = NUMBER OF ELECTRONS

This means that the number of plus charges equals the number of minus charges. They balance each other. Because of this, the entire atom has no charge.

The <u>atomic number</u> is also the same as the number of protons.

NUMBER OF PROTONS = ATOMIC NUMBER

Three things, then, are equal: the number of protons, the number of electrons, and the atomic number.

$\boxed{\begin{matrix} P \\ E \\ N \end{matrix}}$ rotons =
lectrons =
umber (atomic)

Remember this. If you know any one of these numbers, you know the number of the other two. They are the <u>same</u>!

UNDERSTANDING THE ATOM

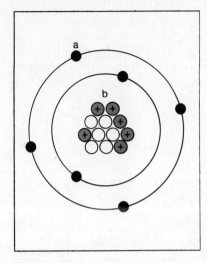

Figure A

Look at Figure A. Answer the questions.

1. The nucleus is labeled _____ .
   a, b

2. The electrons are labeled _____ .
   a, b

3. Name the parts that make up a nucleus.

   _____   _____

4. A proton is _____ than an electron.
   larger, smaller

5. An electron is _____ than a neutron.
   larger, smaller

6. A proton has _____ charge.
   a positive, a negative, no

7. An electron has _____ charge.
   a positive, a negative, no

8. A neutron has _____ charge.
   a positive, a negative, no

UNDERSTANDING ATOMIC MASS

Every kind of atom has an atomic mass. The atomic mass is not a reading from a laboratory balance. It is a way to compare the mass of one atom to that of another atom.

The atomic mass of an atom is the number of parts in its nucleus. The nucleus contains protons and neutrons. Therefore the number of protons plus the number of neutrons is the atomic mass. Electrons are so light that they do not count in atomic mass.

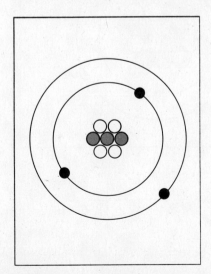

Figure B   *A lithium atom*

- Each proton is given a mass of one.

- Each neutron is given a mass of one.

For example, a lithium atom has 3 protons and 4 neutrons. The atomic mass of a lithium atom is 7 (3 + 4 = 7).

- Each different kind of atom has its own number of protons.

- Each different kind of atom has its own atomic mass.

COMPLETE THE CHART

Complete the chart by filling in the missing information.

Name of Element	Number of Protons	Number of Neutrons	Atomic Mass
Neon	10		20
Cobalt	27		59
Gold	79	118	
Chlorine		18	35
Thorium	90	142	
Lead		125	207
Nickel	28		59
Chromium		28	52
Silicon	14		28
Tungsten	74	110	

WHAT DO THE PICTURES SHOW?

Figures C and D show atoms. Study each figure and answer the questions about each.

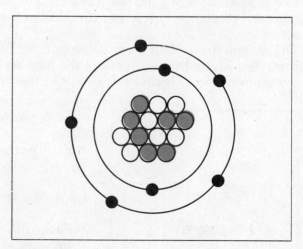

Figure C

1. How many protons does the atom in Figure C have? _____

2. How many neutrons? _____

3. How many electrons? _____

4. What is the atomic mass of this atom? _____

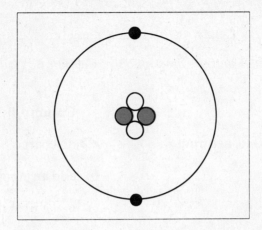

Figure D

5. How many protons does the atom in Figure D have? _____

6. How many neutrons? _____

7. How many electrons? _____

8. What is the atomic mass of this atom? _____

FILL IN THE BLANK

Complete each statement using a term or terms from the list below. Write your answers in the spaces provided. Some words may be used more than once.

positive	no	neutrons	atomic number
atoms	one	circle	electrons
negative	protons		

1. All matter is made up of tiny _____ .

2. The three main parts of an atom are _____ , _____ , and

   _____ .

3. A nucleus is made up of _____ and _____ .

4. Electrons _____ the nucleus.

5. A proton has a _____ charge; an electron has a _____

   charge; a neutron has _____ charge.

6. Protons = electrons = _____ .

7. The atomic mass of an atom is the number of its _____ and

   _____ .

8. Each proton or neutron is given a mass of _____ .

9. In figuring atomic mass, we do not count the mass of an atom's _____ .

11

MATCHING

Match each term in Column A with its description in Column B. Write the correct letter in the space provided.

Column A

_____ 1. protons and neutrons

_____ 2. electron

_____ 3. proton

_____ 4. neutron

_____ 5. to find atomic mass

Column B

a) no charge

b) add an atom's protons and neutrons

c) make up a nucleus

d) positive charge

e) negative charge

WORD SEARCH

The list on the left contains words that you have used in this Lesson. Find and circle each word where it appears in the box. The spelling may go in any direction: up, down, left, right, or diagonally.

PROTONS

NEUTRONS

ELECTRONS

POSITIVE

NEGATIVE

NUCLEUS

ATOMIC

ELEMENT

A	S	E	M	E	R	I	L	E	D	A	P
C	N	V	Q	U	L	O	L	A	N	G	R
T	O	I	U	S	U	E	L	C	U	N	C
N	R	T	O	P	C	L	M	O	S	I	A
O	T	I	G	T	F	Y	I	E	M	O	N
B	U	S	R	P	R	O	T	O	N	S	K
R	E	O	S	I	L	G	T	Y	N	T	I
U	N	P	N	E	G	A	T	I	V	E	J
S	E	F	M	O	A	P	H	E	N	L	E

How are the elements listed in special order?

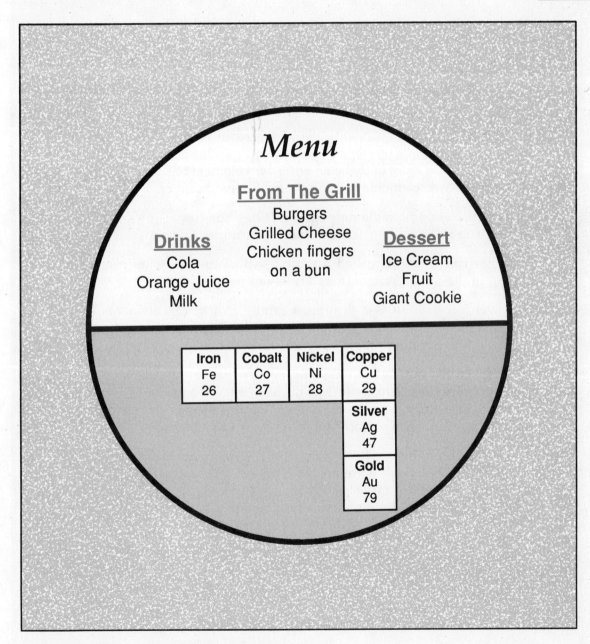

periodic table: a chart of the elements
properties: anything about matter that helps identify it

LESSON 3 | How are the elements listed in special order?

There are many ways to organize information. One way is to use a chart. A chart can be used to show many facts in a small space. All the known elements are listed in a special chart called the **periodic table**.

In the periodic table, elements are arranged in order of their atomic numbers. The <u>atomic number</u> of an element is the number of protons in the nucleus of an atom of that element. Every element has its own atomic number. No two elements have the same atomic number.

Look at the periodic table on page 15. It has horizontal rows that run from left to right and vertical columns that run up and down.

Each horizontal row is called a period. All of the elements in a row belong to the same period. There are seven periods.

Each vertical column is a group, or family. All of the elements in a column belong to the same group. For example, all of the elements in the left-hand column of the table belong to Group 1.

Elements in the same group have properties that are the same or very similar. **Properties** help us to identify elements. Color, smell, state of matter, and density are examples of some properties. Each group takes up one column in the periodic table.

An element is either a <u>metal</u> or <u>nonmetal</u>. The elements listed on the left side of the periodic table are metals. Those listed on the right side are nonmetals. There are more metals than non-metals. A heavy line that looks like stair steps divides metals from nonmetals. Hydrogen, the first element, is in a metals group because it shares some of the properties of metals.

Figure A

Use this periodic table to help you answer each exercise. You can find the names of the elements on the complete periodic table on pages 166-167.

1. List the atomic numbers of the elements in period 2. _____

   _____

2. Write the names and symbols of these elements. _____

   _____

   _____

3. Which of these elements are metals? _____

4. Which of these elements are nonmetals? _____

   _____

5. Name the lightest element in period 2. _____

6. Name the heaviest element in period 2. _____

7. To which group does each of these elements belong?

   a) lithium _____   e) nitrogen _____

   b) beryllium _____   f) oxygen _____

   c) boron _____   g) fluorine _____

   d) carbon _____   h) neon _____

8. List the atomic numbers of the elements in period 3. _____

_____

9. Write the names and symbols of these elements. _____

_____

_____

10. Which of these elements are metals? _____

11. Name the lightest element in period 3. _____

12. Name the heaviest element in period 3. _____

13. To which group does each of these elements belong?

a)	sulfur _____		**e)**	silicon _____
b)	sodium _____		**f)**	magnesium _____
c)	aluminum _____		**g)**	chlorine _____
d)	argon _____		**h)**	phosphorus _____

14. Name the elements in group 12. _____

15. Which element in this group is the heaviest? _____

16. Which element in this group is the lightest? _____

The symbol for iron is Fe. Find iron on the periodic table.

17. What is the atomic number of iron? _____

18. To which period does iron belong? _____

19. To which group does iron belong? _____

20. Name the elements that have many properties like iron. _____

_____

21. To which period does calcium belong? _____

22. To which group does calcium belong? _____

23. List the names and symbols of the elements that have properties similar to calcium.

_____

24. Which of these elements is the lightest? _____

25. Which of these elements is the heaviest? _____

COMPLETE THE CHART

Complete the chart by filling in the missing information. The first row has been done for you.

	Element	Symbol	Atomic Number	Period	Group
1.	Sodium	Na	11	3	1
2.		O			
3.	Krypton				18
4.			79		
5.				5	17
6.				4	11

COMPLETE THE CHART

Complete the chart by filling in the missing information. Hint: you may need the periodic table on pages 166-167.

	Name of Element	Symbol	Atomic Number	Number of Protons	Number of Electrons
1.	Nitrogen				
2.			20		
3.				19	
4.					14
5.				47	
6.	Sulfur				
7.			80		
8.					28

MATCHING

Match each term in Column A with its description in Column B. Write the correct letter in the space provided.

Column A

_____ 1. metals and nonmetals

_____ 2. periodic table

_____ 3. atomic number

_____ 4. group of elements

_____ 5. period of elements

Column B

a) tells how elements are arranged in order

b) in the same row down

c) the chart of the elements

d) in the same row across

e) the two kinds of elements

ROUNDING OFF ATOMIC WEIGHTS

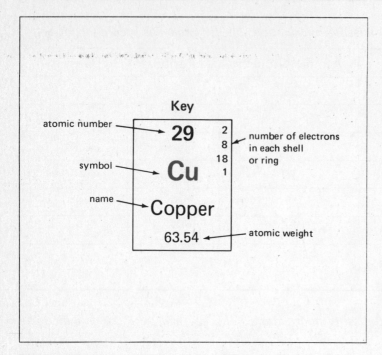

Key

atomic number → **29**   2 ← number of electrons
                   8   in each shell
             18   or ring
symbol → **Cu**   1

name → Copper

63.54 ← atomic weight

This is the "key" to reading the full periodic table on pages 166-167.

Copper has been chosen. Any other element could have been chosen.

Notice that the atomic mass of copper is 63.54. This is a whole number followed by two decimals. Most atomic masses have decimals. In this lesson, we round off the decimal to its nearest whole number. If the decimal is 0.5 or more, round off to the next higher number. If the decimal is less than 0.5, round down.

Figure B

COMPLETE THE CHART

Complete the chart by filling in the missing information.

	Element	Listed Atomic Mass	Rounded-Off Atomic Mass
1.	Copper	63.54	
2.	Calcium	40.08	
3.	Fluorine	18.99	
4.	Strontium	87.62	
5.	Barium	137.34	
6.	Titanium	47.90	
7.	Magnesium	24.31	
8.	Argon	39.94	
9.	Erbium	167.26	
10.	Zirconium	91.22	

FILL IN THE BLANK

Complete each statement using a term or terms from the list below. Write your answers in the spaces provided.

heavier	group	period
nonmetal	periodic table	atomic
more	left	right
atomic number	metal	properties
family	lighter	

1. The chart that lists the elements in an organized way is called the

   _____ .

2. The periodic table lists the elements according to _____ .

3. The number that tells us where an element ranks in mass is called the

   _____ mass.

4. The lower the atomic mass, the _____ the element; the higher the

   atomic mass, the _____ the element.

5. Elements in the same row across belong to the same _____ .

6. Elements in the same column down belong to the same _____ or

   _____ .

7. Elements in the same group or family share important _____ .

8. An element is identified as either a _____ or a _____ .

9. On the periodic table, metals are on the _____ . Nonmetals are on

   the _____ .

10. There are _____ metals than nonmetals.

TWO SPECIAL GROUPS

There are two special groups of elements that are at the opposite ends of the periodic table. The one at the far right is called the noble gases. The one at the far left is called the alkali metals.

The alkali metals

Look at group 1 in the periodic table. None of these elements is found free in nature. Their atoms are always linked with atoms of other elements. This means that the alkali metal elements are always part of compounds.

The alkali metals are lithium, sodium, potassium, rubidium, cesium, and francium. When they are separated from compounds, they are soft, light metals that react easily at room temperature with water vapor in the air. They don't last long as pure elements unless tightly sealed in a container. Hydrogen is not included among the alkali metals. This is because it has some properties different from the other elements in group 1.

The noble gases

Look at group 18 in the periodic table. In nature these elements rarely combine with other elements to form compounds. For this reason, scientists call these elements inert.

The elements in group 18 are helium, neon, argon, krypton, xenon, and radon. All are gases at room temperature. They are found in very small amounts in earth's atmosphere. Argon is the most common of the group.

In which group are the elements gases at

room temperature? _____

In which group are the elements always linked with others to form compounds?

_____

Which element has more electrons,

sodium or neon? _____

Which element is never found free in

nature, sodium or neon? _____

Which element never forms compounds in nature, potassium or argon?

_____

Figure C *Electric signs with neon*

How are electrons arranged around the nucleus?

4

shell: a level outside the nucleus in which electrons move.

LESSON 4 | How are electrons arranged around the nucleus?

Scientists once thought that electrons circled the nucleus in an orbit, the way earth circles the sun. Now scientists know that electrons don't move in fixed orbits. They think that electrons change their positions very quickly. Rapid electron movements form clouds around the nucleus. This means that electron paths have no clear lines or edges.

The electrons' movements are arranged into energy levels called shells. Hydrogen and helium have one electron shell. All other atoms have two or more shells.

Each shell is named with a capital letter. The first shell is called the "K" shell. It is closest to the nucleus. The next shell is the "L" shell. The "M" shell comes next. And so on.

Each shell can hold only a certain number of electrons.

The "K" shell can hold 2 electrons.

The "L" shell can hold 8 electrons.

The "M" shell can hold 18 electrons.

The number of shells an atom has depends upon its number of electrons. Each shell must have its full number of electrons before a new shell starts. If there are more electrons than a shell can hold, a new shell starts.

The outer electron shell of most atoms is not full. Only the atoms of the elements of Group 18 have full outer shells.

• Atoms of most <u>metals</u> have <u>fewer than 4</u> outer-shell electrons.

• Atoms of <u>nonmetals</u> usually have <u>4 or more</u> outer-shell electrons.

Figures A and B show how electrons are arranged in two atoms.

Study each figure. Then answer the questions.

Figure A shows a magnesium atom.

The atomic number of magnesium is 12.

Figure A

1. How many electron shells does

   magnesium have? _____

2. What is the first shell called?

   _____

3. How many electrons does the

   first shell have? _____

4. Is the first shell full? _____

5. The K shell is _____ the nucleus.
   <small>closest to, farthest from</small>

6. What is the second shell called? _____

7. Is this the outer shell? _____

8. How many electrons does the second shell have? _____

9. Is the second shell full? _____

10. What is the third shell called? _____

11. How many electrons does the third shell have? _____

12. Is the third shell full? _____

13. Is this the outer shell? _____

14. Magnesium is a _____ .
    <small>metal, nonmetal</small>

15. Why? _____

Find magnesium in the periodic table.

16. Magnesium is found in period _____ , group _____ .

23

Figure B shows a sulfur atom. The atomic number of sulfur is 16.

Figure B

17. How many electron shells does sulfur have? _____

18. What is the first shell called? _____

19. How many electrons does the first shell have? _____

20. Is the first shell full? _____

21. What is the second shell called? _____

22. Is this the outer shell? _____

23. How many electrons does the second shell have? _____

24. Is the second shell full? _____

25. What is the third shell called? _____

26. How many electrons does the third shell have? _____

27. Is the third shell full? _____

28. Is this the outer shell? _____

29. Sulfur is a _____ .
   <u>metal, nonmetal</u>

30. Why? _____

Find sulfur in the periodic table.

31. Sulfur is found in period_____ , group_____ .

COMPLETING SENTENCES

Choose the correct word or term for each statement. Write your choice in the spaces provided.

1. The first electron shell is the _____ shell. It can hold

   _____ electrons.

2. The second electron shell is the _____ shell. It can hold

   _____ electrons.

3. The third electron shell is the _____ shell. It can hold

   _____ electrons.

4. A metal has _____ than 4 outer-shell electrons.

5. A nonmetal has _____ outer-shell electrons.

FILL IN THE ELECTRONS

Decide how many electrons each of these atoms in Figures C through F has. Then draw the electrons in their proper shells. Make a small ball • to show an electron.

REMEMBER [PEN] .

Label each shell that is not already labeled. Then answer the questions next to each diagram. The first exercise has been filled in as an example.

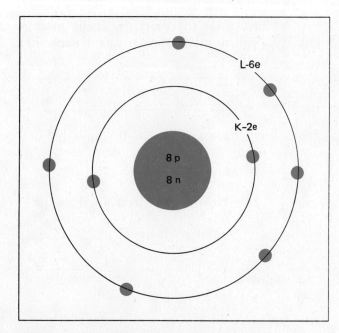

Figure C *Oxygen—atomic number 8*

1. How many electrons does oxygen

   have? _____

2. List the electron shells and the number of electrons in each shell.

   _____

   _____

3. Is the outer shell complete?

   _____

4. How many electrons does the

   outer shell have? _____

5. Oxygen is a _____ .
   metal, nonmetal

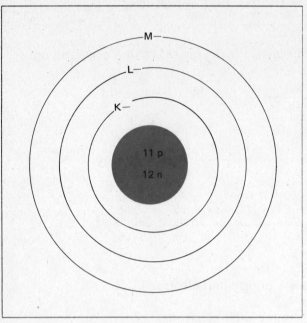

Figure D   *Sodium—atomic number 11*

6. How many electrons does sodium

   have? _____

7. List the electron shells and the
   number of electrons in each shell.

   _____

   _____

   _____

8. Is the outer shell complete?

   _____

9. How many electrons does the

   outer shell have? _____

10. Sodium is a _____ .
    metal, nonmetal

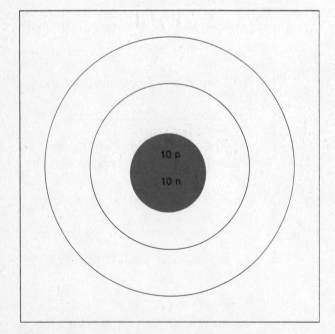

Figure E   *Neon—atomic number 10*

11. How many electrons does neon

    have? _____

12. List the electron shells and the
    number of electrons in each shell.

    _____

    _____

13. Is the outer shell complete?

    _____

14. How many electrons does the

    outer shell have? _____

15. Neon is a _____ .
    metal, nonmetal

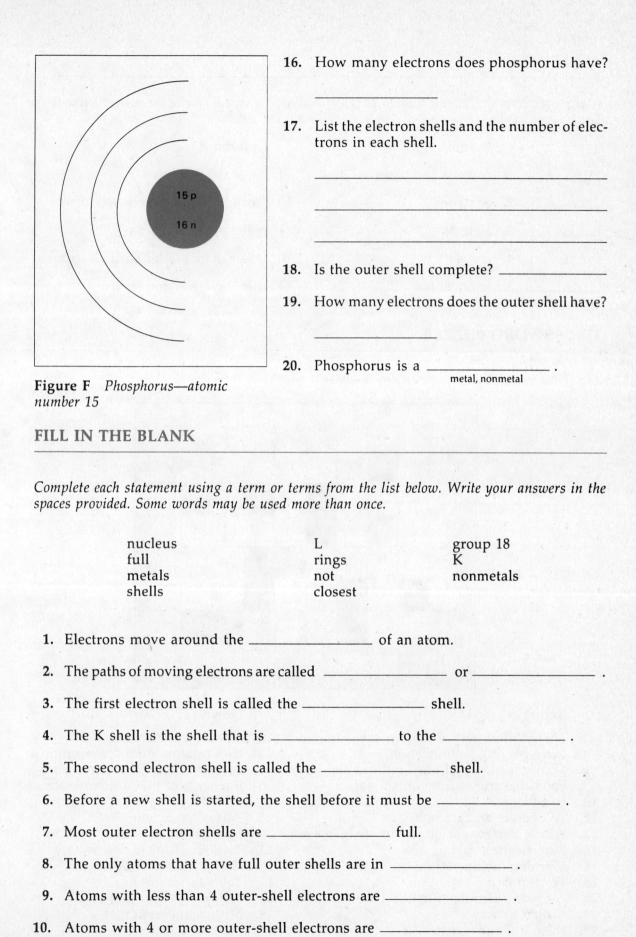

Figure F *Phosphorus—atomic number 15*

16. How many electrons does phosphorus have?

_____

17. List the electron shells and the number of electrons in each shell.

_____

_____

_____

18. Is the outer shell complete? _____

19. How many electrons does the outer shell have?

_____

20. Phosphorus is a _____ .
    metal, nonmetal

FILL IN THE BLANK

Complete each statement using a term or terms from the list below. Write your answers in the spaces provided. Some words may be used more than once.

nucleus	L	group 18
full	rings	K
metals	not	nonmetals
shells	closest	

1. Electrons move around the _____ of an atom.

2. The paths of moving electrons are called _____ or _____ .

3. The first electron shell is called the _____ shell.

4. The K shell is the shell that is _____ to the _____ .

5. The second electron shell is called the _____ shell.

6. Before a new shell is started, the shell before it must be _____ .

7. Most outer electron shells are _____ full.

8. The only atoms that have full outer shells are in _____ .

9. Atoms with less than 4 outer-shell electrons are _____ .

10. Atoms with 4 or more outer-shell electrons are _____ .

27

MATCHING

Match each term in Column A with its description in Column B. Write the correct letter in the space provided.

Column A	Column B
_____ **1.** protons and neutrons	**a)** circle the nucleus
_____ **2.** electrons	**b)** 4 or more outer-shell electrons
_____ **3.** K, L, M	**c)** make up the nucleus
_____ **4.** metals	**d)** fewer than 4 outer-shell electrons
_____ **5.** nonmetals	**e)** first three electron shells

CROSSWORD PUZZLE

Use the clues to complete the crossword puzzle.

Across

1. The smallest part of an element
4. Long-playing (abbreviation)
6. Matter made up of one kind of atom
9. Food that comes from an animal
10. In a place
11. To operate an automobile
12. Where electrons orbit; also found by the sea
15. First electron ring
16. Morning (abbreviation)
18. To stop living
20. A kind of electric current (abbreviation)
21. A man's name
23. What a flame is; not cold
24. K, L, or M for example

Down

2. Needed for chewing
3. Iron or aluminum for example
4. Second and third electron rings
5. Elements of the same row across
7. The last part
8. Part of your foot
9. Face covering
13. Two for a dollar or fifty cents ___
14. Coming after all others
17. Short for mother
19. A bird hatches from one
22. Mister (abbreviation)

How do some compounds form?

5

ion: an atom with a charge

LESSON 5 | How do some compounds form?

You have learned about electron shells. Now use this knowledge to understand how atoms link up to form compounds.

Not all atoms form compounds. Only atoms that have outer shells that are not full form compounds.

The elements of Group 18 have complete outer shells. These atoms usually do not form compounds. All other atoms have outer shells that are not full. All other atoms form compounds.

Atoms form compounds by combining their outer-ring electrons. A total of 8 outer-ring electrons is needed.

Here's an example. An atom with 7 outer-ring electrons will form a compound with an atom with 1 outer-ring electron. (7 + 1 = 8.) (See Figure C.)

An atom with 6 outer-ring electrons will link up with an atom with 2 outer-ring electrons. (6 + 2 = 8.)

In Lesson 4 you learned that:

• Atoms of most metals have fewer than 4 outer-shell electrons.

• Atoms of nonmetals have 4 or more outer-shell electrons.

When forming a compound:

• The metal transfers or lends outer-ring electrons to the nonmetal.

• The nonmetal borrows these electrons.

Here is an easy way to remember this:

M
E
T
A
LEND > ELECTRONS
S

If metals lend electrons, then nonmetals borrow them. A compound has at least one metal and one nonmetal.

UNDERSTANDING HOW A COMPOUND FORMS

Sodium (Na) and chlorine (Cl) link up to form the compound sodium chloride (NaCl)—common table salt. Let's see how it happens.

First, let's look at the atoms of sodium and chlorine.

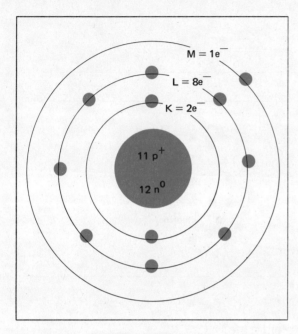

Figure A *A sodium atom*

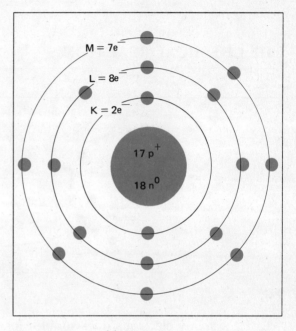

Figure B *A chlorine atom*

1. How many protons does a sodium atom have? _____

2. How many electrons? _____

3. Is the number of protons the same as the number of electrons? _____

4. Is a sodium atom neutral?

_____

5. How many outer-shell electrons does sodium have? _____

6. Is its outer shell full? _____

7. Is sodium a metal or a nonmetal?

_____

8. How many protons does a chlorine atom have? _____

9. How many electrons? _____

10. Is the number of protons the same as the number of electrons? _____

11. Is a chlorine atom neutral?

_____

12. How many outer-shell electrons does chlorine have? _____

13. Is its outer shell full? _____

14. Is chlorine a metal or a nonmetal?

_____

15. Which atom will be an electron lender? _____

16. Which atom will be an electron borrower? _____

17. Add up your answers to questions 5 and 12. _____

Is that the same number of electrons that make up a full shell? _____

THE CHEMICAL REACTION

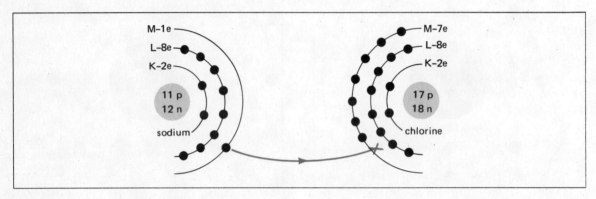

Figure C

1. How many electrons does sodium lose to chlorine? _____

2. Sodium now has _____ electrons and _____ protons.

3. Does sodium still have an equal number of electrons and protons? _____

4. How many electrons does chlorine borrow? _____

5. Chlorine now has _____ electrons and _____ protons.

6. Does chlorine still have an equal number of electrons and protons? _____

Why do sodium and chlorine combine?

When sodium and chlorine combine, sodium LOSES an electron. The chlorine GAINS an electron.

Are sodium and chlorine still neutral atoms? NO! Now, they each have a charge.

The neutral sodium atom lost 1 electron. Therefore, it now has 11 positive charges and only 10 negative charges—or 1 extra positive charge.

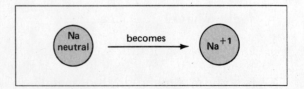

Figure D

Chlorine now has 1 extra negative charge.

We know that atoms are usually neutral. Sodium and chlorine are no longer neutral. They have charges. We call an atom with a charge an **ION** [EYE on].

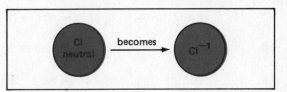

Figure E

> Sodium is a <u>positive</u> ion because its charge is +1.
>
> Chlorine is a <u>negative</u> ion because its charge is –1.

Opposite charges attract. Positive and negative ions are attracted to one another.

The opposite charges hold the sodium and chlorine ions together. Together they form sodium chloride. Sodium chloride is a compound.

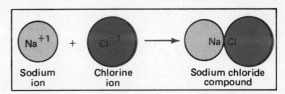

Figure F

LET'S FORM ANOTHER COMPOUND

Look at Figure G. It shows how one magnesium atom combines with two fluorine atoms.

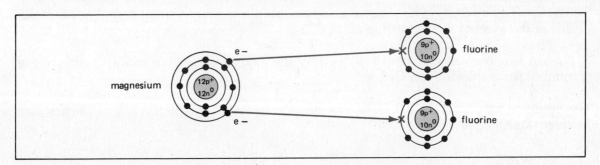

Figure G

1. How many electrons does magnesium lose? _____

2. How many minus charges does magnesium lose? _____

3. How many minus charges does magnesium now have? _____

4. How many plus charges does magnesium now have? _____

5. The magnesium now has a _____ charge.

<small>+2, –2</small>

6. What do we call a charged atom? _____

7. The magnesium is a _____ ion.

<small>positive, negative</small>

8. How many electrons does each fluorine atom gain? _____

9. How many minus charges does each fluorine atom gain? _____

10. How many minus charges does each fluorine atom now have? _____

11. How many plus charges does each fluorine atom now have? _____

12. What charge does each fluorine atom now have? _____
   +1, -1

13. The fluorine is now a _____ ion.
   positive, negative

14. The magnesium and fluorine ions have _____ charges.
   opposite, the same

15. They _____ attract one another.
   do, do not

16. The compound that magnesium and fluorine form is magnesium fluoride. What

   keeps the magnesium fluoride together? _____

   _____

WRITING SYMBOLS FOR IONS

- An atom has no charge. It is shown as a symbol followed by a small zero. For example, this is the symbol for a chlorine atom Cl^0.

- An ion is shown as a symbol followed by the charge value. For example, this is the symbol for a chlorine ion Cl^{-1}.

Use what you have learned about atoms and ions. Complete the information below. The first line has been done for you.

ATOMS		IONS
1. CA^0 ——— loses 2 ——— electrons ⟶		CA^{+2}
2. O^0 ——————— electrons ⟶		O^{-2}
3. K^0 ——————— electrons ⟶		K^{+1}
4. Ag^0 ——————— electrons ⟶		Ag^{+1}
5. F^0 ——————— electrons ⟶		F^{-1}

NOW LET'S TRY IT ANOTHER WAY.

Again, the first line has been done for you.

ATOMS	IONS
6. Al^0 −3 electrons ⟶	_____ Al^{+3}

7. P^0 +3 electrons $\longrightarrow$ _____

8. Li^0 –1 electron $\longrightarrow$ _____

9. Be^0 –2 electrons $\longrightarrow$ _____

10. I^0 +1 electron $\longrightarrow$ _____

COMPLETE THE CHART

Complete the chart by filling in the missing information. The first element, copper, has already been done for you.

	Element	Number of Electrons in Outer Ring	Metal or Nonmetal?	Lends or Borrows Electrons?	Can Lend or Borrow How Many Electrons?
1.	Copper	1	metal	lends	1
2.	Phosphorus				
3.	Iodine				
4.	Vanadium				
5.	Cobalt				
6.	Sodium				
7.	Nitrogen				
8.	Helium				
9.	Gold				
10.	Zinc				

MATCHING

Match each term in Column A with its description in Column B. Write the correct letter in the space provided.

Column A

_____ 1. compound

_____ 2. at least one metal and one nonmetal

_____ 3. 8

_____ 4. metals

_____ 5. nonmetals

Column B

a) needed to form a compound

b) borrow electrons

c) two or more linked-up atoms

d) total number of outer-ring electrons needed to form a compound

e) lend electrons

SCIENCE*EXTRA*

How do you see an atom?

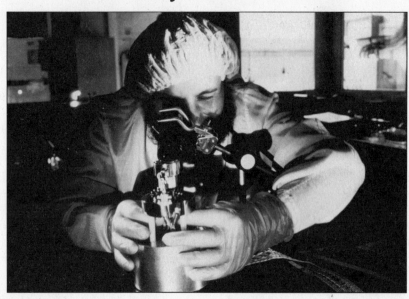

Scientists can now see images of atoms. Something as small as an atom can't be seen by looking through a typical light microscope. This is because light can't be focused upon a single atom. The smallest objects seen through a light microscope are well over one thousand atoms across.

Electron microscopes form images of objects only a few dozen atoms across. These microscopes replace light and lenses with electrons and magnets. A beam of electrons is aimed at an object. The magnets focus the electrons onto the object's surface. Scientists then examine an image on film.

To make an image of a single atom, scientists use a **scanning-tunneling microscope**. It can form images of atoms at the surface of a material. The microscope does this by measuring the electric current produced by electrons in the outermost layer of a material. How does this work?

A tiny probe of metal wire is brought near the surface of the object. Electrons in the surface layer of atoms in the probe approach electrons in the surface layer of the object. When the probe is close enough, its outermost electron orbits overlap the electron orbits of the object. This overlap allows electrons to flow between probe and object.

The probe then measures the current produced by this flow of electrons. Special controls on the microscope allow the operator to move the probe in tiny steps. Each step is less than the diameter of one atom. In this way, the probe scans the surface of the object. A computer uses the probe's measurements of electric current to make an image of atoms.

Scientists have studied atoms for centuries. Now, for the first time, they can see what they look like.

What are the properties of metals?

6

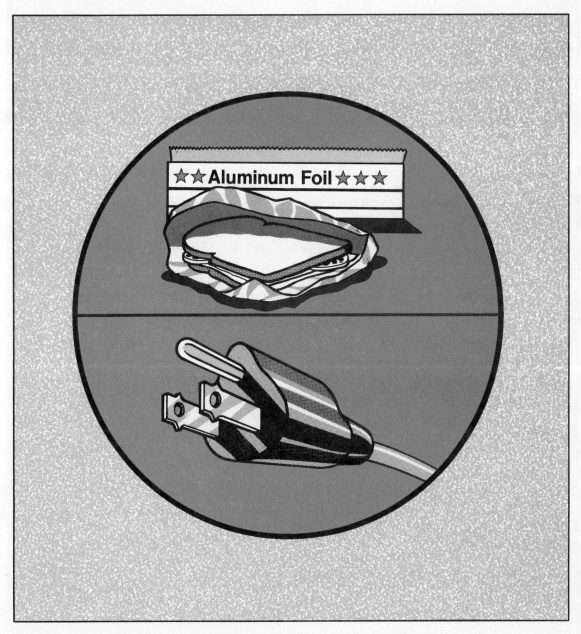

ductile: able to be drawn into thin wire
malleable: able to be thinned out by rolling or hammering without breaking apart

LESSON 6 | What are the properties of metals?

You come in contact with all kinds of matter—paper, plastic, steel, glass, water, air. . . . You have no trouble telling one from another. Each one looks, feels, and behaves in its own special way. Each one has its own properties. Properties help us to identify matter.

No two substances have exactly the same properties. Certain kinds of substances, however, have certain properties that are the same. For example, metals share certain important properties. Let's see what they are.

- Metals are <u>solid</u> at room temperature. There is one exception. Mercury is a liquid.

- Metals are <u>silver-gray in color</u>. There are two exceptions. Gold and copper are yellow to orange-yellow.

- Metals are <u>good conductors of heat and electricity</u>. This means that heat and electricity move easily through metals.

- Metals have a certain shiny look. We call that shine <u>metallic luster</u>.

- Metals are **malleable**. This means that they can be hammered or rolled into thin pieces without breaking.

- Metals are also **ductile**. This means that they can be made into thin wires.

WHAT DO THE PICTURES SHOW?

Each picture shows a property of metal. Which property is it? Write the correct property under each picture. (Answer in complete sentences.)

Figure A

1. Metals are _____

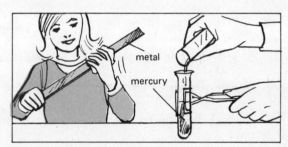

Figure B

2. _____

Figure C

3. _____

Figure D

4. _____

Figure E

5. _____

Figure F

6. _____

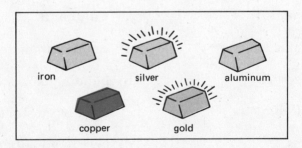

Figure G

7. _____

FILL IN THE BLANK

Complete each statement using a term or terms from the list below. Write your answers in the spaces provided. Some words may be used more than once.

liquid	nonmetals	copper
mercury	atoms	silver-gray
gas	the same	solid
share	metals	properties
gold	conductors of heat	

1. All matter is made up of _____ .

2. The three states of matter are _____ , _____ , and

   _____ .

3. Elements are grouped as _____ and _____ .

4. Elements are identified by certain clues. We call these clues _____ .

5. No two different substances have properties that are all _____ .

6. Certain groups of substances do _____ certain properties.

7. Metals belong to the same group of substances because they share some important

   _____ .

8. Metals are _____ at room temperature except for _____ .

9. Metals are _____ in color except for _____ and

   _____ .

10. A frying pan proves that metals are good _____ .

MATCHING

Match each term in Column A with its description in Column B. Write the correct letter in the space provided.

	Column A	Column B
_____	1. metallic luster	a) can be hammered without breaking
_____	2. properties	b) building blocks of matter
_____	3. malleable	c) color of most metals
_____	4. atoms	d) help to identify matter
_____	5. silver-gray	e) special kind of shine

MORE ON PROPERTIES

Look at Figures H, I, and J. Then answer the questions.

The aluminum foil that you use at home was made in a huge machine like the one in Figure H.

Figure H

1. What property do metals have that makes aluminum foil possible? _____

_____

You have read about seven properties of metals. Figures I and J show two more properties. Can you figure out what they are?

Write your answers by completing the sentence below each figure.

Figure I

2. Most metals are _____

Figure J

3. Most metals are _____

TRUE OR FALSE

In the space provided, write "true" if the sentence is true. Write "false" if the sentence is false.

_____ **1.** A waxed floor has a shine.

_____ **2.** A waxed floor has a metallic luster.

_____ **3.** Mercury is a liquid at room temperature.

_____ **4.** Mercury is a metal.

_____ **5.** All metals are solid.

_____ **6.** Most metals are silver-gray.

_____ **7.** Only metals are silver-gray.

_____ **8.** Gold is silver-gray.

_____ **9.** Wood is ductile.

_____ **10.** Wood is a metal.

WORD SCRAMBLE

Below are several scrambled words you have used in this Lesson. Unscramble the words and write your answers in the spaces provided.

1. LEAMT _____

2. RUSTEL _____

3. CLUDITE _____

4. CYMRRUE _____

5. LEMALEBAL _____

REACHING OUT

The properties of metals and nonmetals are generally opposite. Make a list of some of the properties of nonmetals.

_____

_____

_____

_____

What are oxidation numbers?

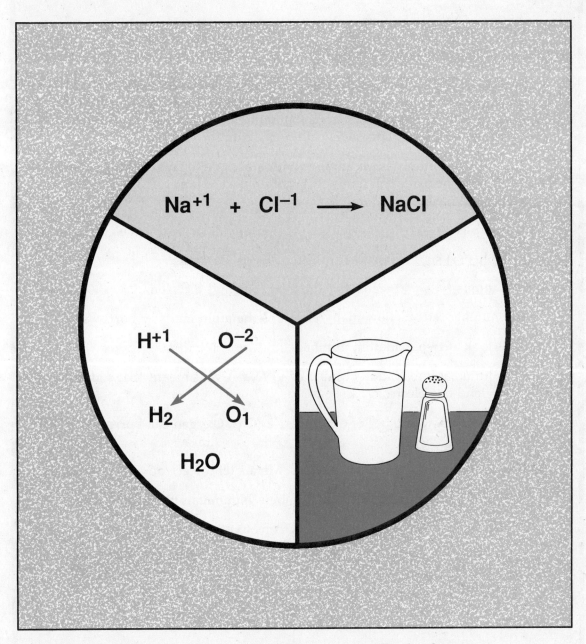

oxidation number: the number of electrons an atom can lend or borrow

LESSON 7 | What are oxidation numbers?

Atoms of metals link up with atoms of nonmetals. They form compounds. When a compound forms, the metal lends outer-ring electrons to the nonmetal. The nonmetal borrows the electrons.

How many electrons does an atom lend or borrow? It depends upon the atom. It also depends upon the compound being formed. Some atoms give up or take on more electrons than others. The number of electrons an atom can lend or borrow is called its **oxidation number**.

An oxidation number is a number with a plus (+) or minus (–) sign in front of it. The oxidation number is written next to the atom it describes, such as Al^{+3}, Mg^{+2}, Br^{-1}, and Se^{-2}.

The sign (+ or –) tells us whether the atom lends or borrows electrons.

- A <u>plus (+) sign</u> means that the atom <u>lends</u> electrons.

- A <u>minus (–) sign</u> means that the atom <u>borrows</u> electrons.

The number tells us <u>how many</u> electrons the atom lends or borrows.

Let's look at two oxidation numbers.

- Sodium has a oxidation number of +1 (Na^{+1}). This means that sodium can lend one electron.

- The oxidation number of oxygen is –2 (O^{-2}). Oxygen can borrow two electrons.

Metals have plus oxidation numbers. Metals lend electrons.

Nonmetals have minus oxidation numbers. Nonmetals borrow electrons.

A nonmetal will borrow enough electrons to complete its outer shell.

Many elements have more than one oxidation number. In fact, some elements have both plus and minus oxidation numbers. Sometimes they lend electrons. Sometimes they borrow electrons.

USING THE PERIODIC TABLE TO FIND OXIDATION NUMBERS

You can find the oxidation numbers of many elements by looking at the periodic table.

FINDING THE OXIDATION NUMBER OF A METAL

This is the simplest oxidation number to find. In many cases, the oxidation number of a metal is the same as the number of electrons in its outer shell.

A metal lends (loses) electrons. Therefore, its oxidation number is plus (+).

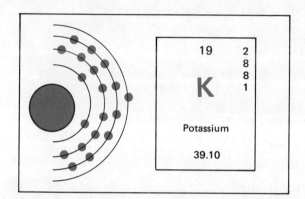

Figure A shows an example.

Potassium has 1 outer-shell electron.

Potassium lends this single electron.

The oxidation number of potassium is +1 (K^{+1}).

Figure A

FINDING THE OXIDATION NUMBER OF A NONMETAL

This is simple too. Here is what to do:

• Check the number of electrons in the outer shell.

• Figure out how many electrons that atom needs to make a stable outer shell (in most cases, 8 electrons). That number is the oxidation number.

A nonmetal will add, or borrow, these electrons. Therefore, its oxidation number is minus (–).

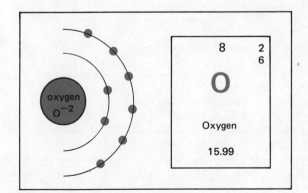

Figure B shows an example.

Oxygen has 6 outer-shell electrons.

Oxygen needs 2 more electrons to make its outer shell stable (8 – 6 = 2).

Oxygen will borrow (gain) these 2 electrons.

The oxidation number of oxygen is –2 (O^{-2}).

Figure B

4 2
2
Be
Beryllium
9.01

Figure C

1. How many outer-shell electrons does beryllium have? _____

2. Beryllium is a _____ .
   metal, nonmetal

3. Beryllium _____ electrons.
   lends, borrows

4. How many electrons can beryllium lend? _____

5. What is the oxidation number of beryllium? _____

16 2
8
6
S
Sulfur
32.06

Figure D

6. a) How many outer-shell electrons does sulfur have? _____

   b) Is this a stable shell? _____

   c) How many electrons are needed to make a stable shell? _____

7. Sulfur is a _____ .
   metal, nonmetal

8. Sulfur _____ electrons.
   lends, borrows

9. How many electrons can sulfur borrow? _____

10. What is the oxidation number of sulfur? _____

WORKING WITH OXIDATION NUMBERS

Ten elements and their oxidation numbers are listed below. Study each one. Then fill in the chart. The first line has been filled in for you.

	Element	Symbol and oxidation number	Metal or nonmetal	Lends or borrow electrons?	Lends or borrows how many electrons?
1.	Oxygen	O^{-2}	Nonmetal	borrows	2
2.	Calcium	Ca^{+2}			
3.	Aluminum	Al^{+3}			
4.	Bromine	Br^{-1}			
5.	Nitrogen	N^{-3}			
6.	Zinc	Zn^{+2}			
7.	Lithium	Li^{+1}			
8.	Sulfur	S^{-2}			
9.	Phosphorus	P^{-3}			
10.	Silver	Ag^{+1}			

USING OXIDATION NUMBERS TO FIND FORMULAS

You can use oxidation numbers to figure out the formula for any simple compound. All you need to know are the symbols and the oxidation numbers of the elements that make up the compound. JUST CRISS-CROSS THE OXIDATION NUMBERS.

Water is made up of hydrogen (H) and oxygen (O). The oxidation number of hydrogen is +1 (H^{+1}). The oxidation number of oxygen is –2 (O^{-2}).

For example, this is how to write the formula for water:

Step 1 Write down the symbol of each element. List the element with the plus (+) oxidation number first.

$$H \quad O$$

Step 2 Write down the oxidation number of each element next to the element like this:

$$H^+ \quad O^{-2}$$

Step 3 Criss-cross the <u>numbers</u> in the oxidation number only. Leave out the signs.

$$H^{+1} \quad O^{-2}$$

$$H_2 \quad O_1 = H_2O_1$$

One molecule of water, then, contains 2 atoms of hydrogen and 1 atom of oxygen.

In a final formula, we do not write any 1's. So the formula for water is H_2O.

Table salt is made up of atoms of sodium (Na) and chlorine (Cl). The oxidation number of sodium is +1 (Na^{+1}). The oxidation number of chlorine is –1 (Cl^{-1}).

Write it down. $Na^{+1}Cl^{-1}$

Cross over the numbers. $Na^{+1}Cl^{-1}$
                           $Na_1 Cl_1$

Cancel out the ones. $Na_{\cancel{1}}Cl_{\cancel{1}}$

The formula for table salt is **NaCl**.

Table salt is sodium chloride. One molecule of sodium chloride has 1 atom of sodium and 1 atom of chlorine. Altogether one molecule of salt contains 2 atoms.

What do you do if both oxidation numbers (not the signs) are the same? This is the case when magnesium and oxygen combine.

$$Mg^{+2}O^{-2}$$
$$Mg_2 O_2 = Mg_2O_2$$

Cancel out both numbers like this: $Mg_{\cancel{2}}O_{\cancel{2}}$.

The formula, then is **MgO**.

There are some compounds where the numbers are not canceled out, but these compounds will not be covered in this book.

Work these out by yourself. It's easy! Just do one step at a time.

Calcium (Ca) links up with iodine (I) to form a compound called calcium iodide.

The oxidation number of calcium is +2 (Ca^{+2}). The oxidation number of iodine is –1 (I^{-1}).

1. Write down each element and its oxidation number. (Remember, the + oxidation number comes first.)

   1. [ ]

2. Cross over the numbers.

   2. [ ]

3. Cancel out numbers. (Skip if not needed.)

   3. [ ]

4. Write the formula.

   4. [ ]

5. What is the name of this compound? _____

6. One molecule of calcium iodide has _____ atom(s) of calcium and _____ atom(s) of iodine.

7. Altogether, how many atoms does one molecule of calcium iodide have? _____

Gold and sulfur combine to form the compound gold sulfide.

The oxidation number of gold is +1 (Au^{+1}). The oxidation number of sulfur is –2 (S^{-2}).

8. Write down each element and its oxidation number.

   8. [ ]

9. Cross over numbers.

   9. [ ]

10. Cancel out numbers. (Skip if not needed.).

    10. [ ]

11. Write the formula.

    11. [ ]

12. What is the name of this compound? _____

13. One molecule of gold sulfide has _____ atom(s) of gold and _____ atom(s) of sulfur.

14. Altogether, how many atoms does one molecule of gold sulfide have? _____

FILL IN THE BLANK

Complete each statement using a term or terms from the list below. Write your answers in the spaces provided. Some words may be used more than once.

<blockquote>
lend   oxidation number   number
more than one   borrow   stable outer shell
how many   loses   compounds
+ or – sign   gains
</blockquote>

1. Metals link up with nonmetals to form _____ .

2. When forming compounds, metals _____ electrons. Nonmetals

   _____ electrons.

3. An atom's _____ tells how many electrons the atom can lend or borrow.

4. A oxidation number is written as a _____ with a _____ in front of it.

5. The number tells us _____ electrons an atom gains or loses.

6. The sign tells us whether the atom will _____ or _____ electrons.

7. A atom with a plus (+) oxidation number lends electrons. Another way of saying

   this is: An atom with a plus oxidation number _____ electrons.

8. An atom with a minus (–) oxidation number borrows electrons. Another way of

   saying this is: An atom with a minus oxidation number _____ electrons.

9. A nonmetal will borrow enough electrons to give a _____ .

10. Many elements have _____ oxidation number.

MATCHING

Match each term in Column A with its description in Column B. Write the correct letter in the space provided.

Column A	Column B
_____ 1. compound	a) tells how many electrons an atom can lend or borrow
_____ 2. 2, 8, or 18 outer-shell electrons	b) lends electrons
_____ 3. oxidation number	c) at least one metal and one nonmetal
_____ 4. + oxidation number atom	d) borrows electrons
_____ 5. – oxidation number atom	e) stable outer shell

COMPLETE THE CHART

Write the correct formulas in the spaces below. Three formulas have been written for you.

NONMETALS

METALS		Cl^{-1}	S^{-2}	O^{-2}	I^{-1}	Br^{-1}
	H^{+1}	1. HCl	2.	3. H_2O	4.	5.
	Al^{+3}	6.	7.	8.	9. AlI_3	10.
	Ca^{+2}	11.	12.	13.	14.	15.
	Cu^{+1}	16.	17.	18.	19.	20.
	Mg^{+2}	21.	22.	23.	24.	25.
	Na^{+1}	26.	27.	28.	29.	30.

REACHING OUT

Oxidation numbers can help you find a formula. It goes the other way too. A formula can help you find the oxidation number of the elements in a compound.

For example, NiI_2 is the formula for nickel iodide. The formula tells us that:

• The oxidation number of nickel is +2. (Remember, the metal always goes first—and a metal has a positive (+) oxidation number.)

• The oxidation number of iodine is –1.

Six compounds are listed below. Figure out the oxidation number of the elements in each compound. The first one has been done for you.

	Formula	Atoms and Their Oxidation Numbers	
1.	CaF_2	Ca^{+2}	F^{-1}
2.	KBr		
3.	Mg_3N_2		
4.	CCl_4		
5.	H_2S		
6.	$FeCl_3$		

50

What is a polyatomic ion?

8

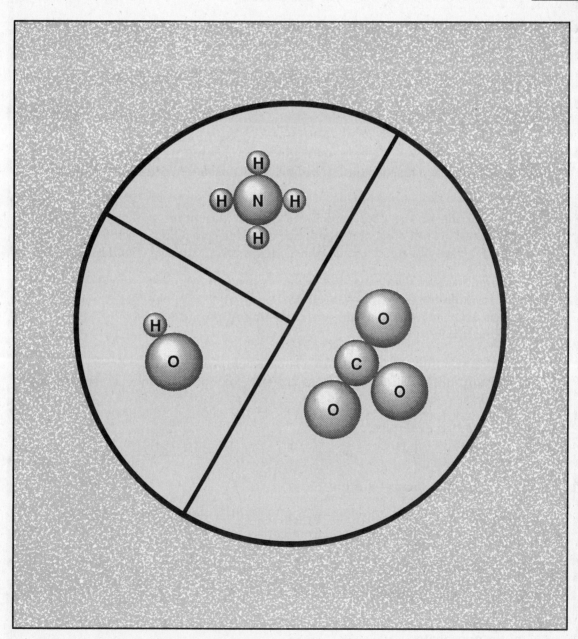

polyatomic [PAHL-i-uh-tahm-ik] **ion:** group of atoms that acts as a single atom
subscript: number written to the lower right of a chemical symbol

LESSON 8 | What is a polyatomic ion?

Many friends are "extra" good friends. They get together very often. And then, they seem to act like one person.

Certain elements are like that. They "get together" whenever possible. And then, they act as if they were one element.

A group of atoms that behaves like a single atom is called a **polyatomic** [PAHL-i-uh-tahm-ik] **ion** A polyatomic ion has its own oxidation number.

Eight common radicals along with their oxidation number are listed on the facing page. All the common radicals have a minus oxidation number except one. The ammonium radical (NH_4) has a +1 oxidation number $(NH_4)^{+1}$.

The radicals in the chart are listed within parenthesis like (OH). A parenthesis is not always needed. For example, the (OH) in the formula Na(OH) does not need a parenthesis. It can be written as NaOH.

A parenthesis is always needed when a subscript follows a radical. Take this formula for example—$Ca(OH)_2$. The small 2 after the OH is a **subscript**. It means that one molecule of this compound has two hydroxyl (OH) radicals.

How do you find the formula for a simple compound that has one or eve two radicals? It's simple. Just criss-cross the oxidation numbers—just as you did last lesson.

Here are two examples.

1. $CA^2 + (CO_3)^{-2}$

   $Ca_2(CO_3)_2$ (cancel out the 2's)

The final formula is $Ca(CO_3)$ or $CaCO_3$. Either one may be used. The name for this compound is calcium carbonate.

2. $(NH_4)^{+1} + (PO_4)^{-3}$

   $(NH_4)_3(PO_4)_1$ (cancel out the 1)

The final formula is $(NH_4)_3PO_4$. The name for this compound is ammonium phosphate.

UNDERSTANDING POLYATOMIC IONS

Radical	Formula and Oxidation Number
Ammonium	$(NH_4)^{+1}$
Bicarbonate	$(HCO_3)^{-1}$
Hydroxyl	$(OH)^{-1}$
Nitrate	$(NO_3)^{-1}$

Radical	Formula and Oxidation Number
Carbonate	$(CO_3)^{-2}$
Sulfite	$(SO_3)^{-2}$
Sulfate	$(SO_4)^{-2}$
Phosphate	$(PO_4)^{-3}$

The chart above shows eight common polyatomic ions.

Now look at the chart below. The names of the eight radicals are listed in Column A.

Do the following:

- In Column B, write the formula of each polyatomic ion.
- In Column C, list the elements that make up each radical and the number of atoms of each element.
- In Column D, list the oxidation number of each polyatomic ion.

The first one has been completed for you.

	A Radical Name	B Formula	C Elements and Number of Atoms of Each	D Oxidation Number
1.	Sulfate	SO_4	Sulfur—1 atom Oxygen—4 atoms	−2
2.	Bicarbonate			
3.	Nitrate			
4.	Ammonium			
5.	Phosphate			
6.	Carbonate			
7.	Hydroxyl			
8.	Sulfite			

NAMING COMPOUNDS

Eight compounds are listed in the chart below. Each one contains at least one radical. Name each compound. Choose from the list below.

Note: In a compound, the hydroxyl radical (OH) is called hydroxide.

calcium carbonate
ammonium nitrate
potassium hydroxide
copper nitrate

sodium sulfate
ammonium chloride
silver nitrate
ammonium hydroxide

	Formula	Name
1.	$Ag(NO_3)$	
2.	$K(OH)$	
3.	NH_4Cl	
4.	$Ca(CO_3)$	
5.	$Cu(NO_3)_2$	
6.	$NH_4(OH)$	
7.	$NH_4(NO_3)$	
8.	$Na_2(SO_4)$	

WRITING FORMULAS

Write the correct formulas in the chart below. Two formulas have been written for you.

Remember: The plus oxidation number goes first. Then criss-cross the oxidation numbers.

For example: $K^{+1} + (PO_4)^{-3}$

$K_3(PO_4)_1$

	$(OH)^{-1}$	$(NO_3)^{-1}$	$(PO_4)^{-3}$	$(HCO_3)^{-1}$	$(SO_4)^{-2}$
K^{+1}	1.	2.	3. $K_3(PO_4)$	4.	5.
Mg^{+2}	6.	7. $Mg(NO_3)_2$	8.	9.	10.
H^{+1}	11.	12.	13.	14.	15.

What is a polyvalent element?

9

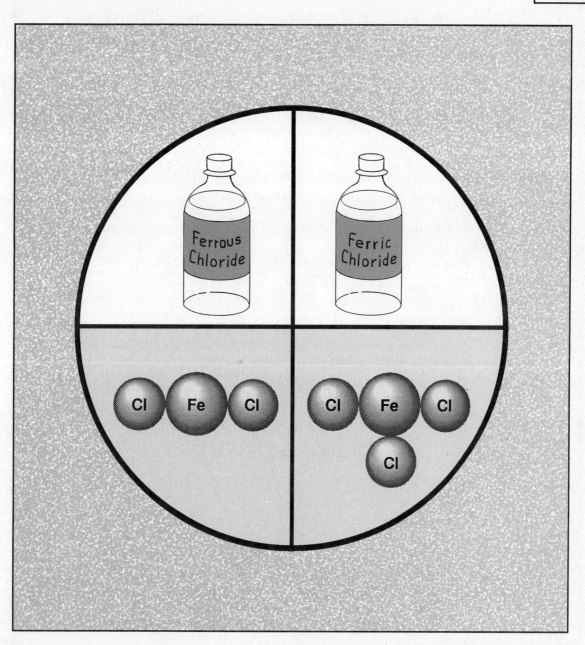

polyvalent [pahl-i-VAY-lunt]: having more than one oxidation number

LESSON 9 | What is a polyvalent element?

All elements have an oxidation number. Many elements have more than one oxidation number. Elements with more than one oxidation number are called **polyvalent** [pahl-i-VAY-lunt]. Many elements are polyvalent. Iron (Fe), for example, has an oxidation number of +2 (Fe^{+2}). Iron can also have an oxidation number of +3 (Fe^{+3}).

A polyvalent metal can form more than one kind of compound with the same nonmetal.

For example, iron (Fe) combines with chlorine (Cl^{-1}). The compound that forms can be either $FeCl_2$ or $FeCl_3$. Which one? It depends upon the oxidation number of the iron.

If iron with an oxidation number of +2 (Fe^{+2}) takes part in the reaction we get $FeCl_2$.

$FeCl_2$ is called FERROUS chloride. The *ferr-* part comes from *ferre*, the Latin word for iron. The *-ous* ending tells us that iron with the lower oxidation number took part in the reaction.

Ferrous chloride is also called iron II chloride. The Roman numeral tells us the oxidation number of a polyvalent metal. Iron II means that the oxidation number of iron in ferrous chloride is +2.

If iron with an oxidation number of +3 (Fe^{+3}) takes part in the reaction we get $FeCl_3$.

$FeCl_3$ is called FERRIC chloride. The *-ic* ending tells us that iron with the higher oxidation number iron took part in the reaction.

Ferric chloride is also called iron III chloride. What does iron III mean?

WORKING WITH POLYVALENT ELEMENTS

The chart below shows five elements that are polyvalent. It shows the different oxidation numbers and the names that their compounds have.

OXIDATION NUMBERS OF METALS

Metal	Lower Oxidation Number	Name	Higher Oxidation Number	Name
Iron	Fe^{+2}	ferrous	Fe^{+3}	ferric
Mercury	Hg^{+1}	mercurous	Hg^{+2}	mercuric
Copper	Cu^{+1}	cuprous	Cu^{+2}	cupric
Gold	Au^{+1}	aurous	Au^{+3}	auric
Tin	Sn^{+2}	stannous	Sn^{+4}	stannic

1. How many oxidation numbers does each of these elements have? _____

2. The name of each lower oxidation number compound ends with _____ .
   -ous, -ic

3. The name of each higher oxidation number compounds ends with _____ .
   -ous, -ic

In a compound, "ferr-" means iron. Which elements do these stand for?

4. stann- _____   5. cupr- _____   6. aur- _____

Write the symbols and valences on the chart below. The first one has been done for you.

	Element	Symbol	Oxidation Numbers	
7.	Iron	Fe	+2	+3
8.	Tin			
9.	Gold			
10.	Mercury			
11.	Copper			

WRITING FORMULAS

Write the formula for each combination. Then answer the questions.

1. a) $Fe^{+2} + I^{-1} \longrightarrow$

$$FeI_2$$

b) The name of this compound is _____ iodide.

ferrous, ferric

2. a) $Hg^{+2} + Br^{-1} \longrightarrow$

b) The name of this compound is _____ bromide.

mercurous, mercuric

3. a) $Sn^{+2} + F^{-1} \longrightarrow$

b) The name of this compound is _____ fluoride.

stannous, stannic

4. a) $Cu^{+1} + S^{-2} \longrightarrow$

b) The name of this compound is _____ sulfide.

cuprous, cupric

REACHING OUT

Which compound on this page is found in a familiar household product?

_____

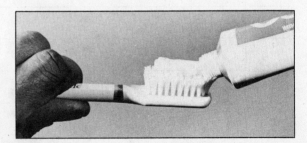

Figure A

What is formula mass? 10

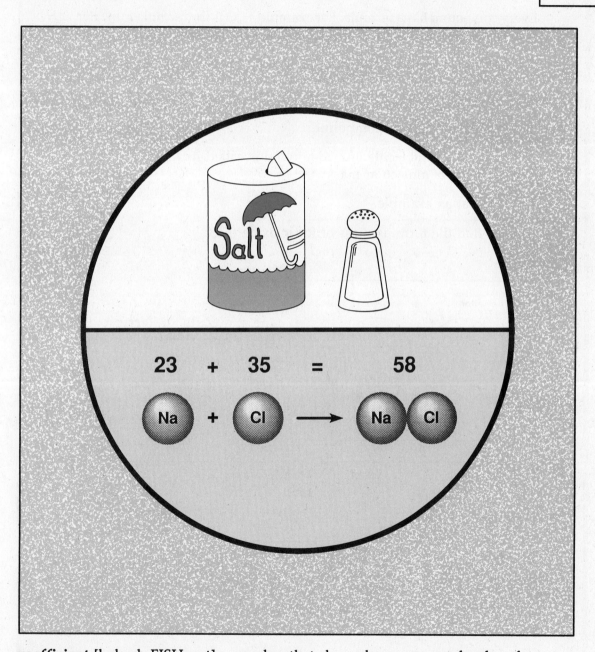

coefficient [koh-uh-FISH-unt]:   number that shows how many molecules of a
    substance are involved in a chemical reaction
formula mass: sum of the mass numbers of all the atoms in a molecule

LESSON 10 | What is formula mass?

Every compound has a formula. For example, H_2O is the formula for water. NaCl is the formula for table salt. $C_{12}H_{22}O_{11}$ is the formula for table sugar.

Compounds are made of atoms. Atoms have mass. Therefore, compounds have mass.

If we add up the mass of all the atoms in a compound, we find the mass of one molecule of that compound.

The mass of one molecule of a compound is called its formula mass. It also is called its molecular mass.

Let's look at an example.

How to find the formula mass of ferric oxide (Fe_2O_3):

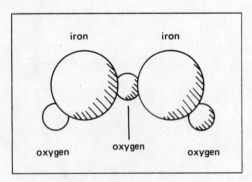

One molecule of ferric oxide (Fe_2O_3) has 2 atoms of iron and 3 atoms of oxygen.

Element	Number of atoms		Atomic mass rounded off (mass of one atom)	Total mass of atoms
Iron	2	×	56	112
Oxygen	3	×	16	48

FORMULA MASS (mass of one molecule of Fe_2O_3) = 160

WORKING WITH FORMULA MASSES

Find the formula (molecular) mass of each compound that follows. Look up the symbol names and atomic masses. (You probably know the names of most of these symbols.)

1. Sulfuric acid H_2SO_4

Element	Number of atoms		Atomic mass	Total mass of atoms
Hydrogen	2	×		
Sulfur	1	×		
Oxygen	4	×		

Formula mass = _____

2. Sucrose (table sugar) $C_{12}H_{22}O_{11}$

Element	Number of atoms	Atomic mass	Total mass of atoms

Formula mass = _____

THE INSIDE STORY

Now let's try slightly more difficult compounds. (You will find that they are not really more difficult.) How do you handle a compound with a polyatomic ion? Molecules with polyatomic ions often have a part in parentheses and this part is followed by a subscript. $Ca(NO_3)_2$ (calcium nitrate) is a example.

Step 1 Find the number of atoms of each element.

The calcium **Ca** is <u>outside</u> the parentheses. No special figuring is needed. This formula has one atom of calcium.

The nitrate **$(NO_3)_2$** needs some very easy figuring. Simply multiply the number of atoms of each element within the parentheses by the subscript ($_2$).

So we have

Number of atoms in parentheses ↘   ↙ Subscript

$$N = 1 \times \boxed{2} = 2 \text{ atoms}$$
$$O = 3 \times \boxed{2} = 7 \text{ atoms}$$

Step 2 Now we can find the formula mass.

Element	Number of atoms	Atomic mass	Total mass of atoms
Calcium	1	40	40
Nitrogen	2	14	28
Oxygen	6	16	96

Formula Mass of one molecule of $Ca(NO_3)_2$ =   164

Four formulas are given. Figure out the number of atoms of each element.

1. $Fe(NO_3)_2$ Fe _____

N _____

O _____

2. $Al_2(SO_4)_3$ Al _____

S _____

O _____

Now that you know how to handle parentheses and subscripts, figure out the formula mass of each formula listed below. Find the names of the elements in the periodic table at the end of the book.

3. $Ca(OH)_2$

Element	Number of atoms	Atomic mass	Total mass of atoms
Calcium	1		
Oxygen	2		
Hydrogen	2		

Formula mass = _____

4. $Hg_2(SCN)_2$ (S, C, and N are separate elements. Naturally! Each one is a capital letter.)

Element	Number of atoms	Atomic mass	Total mass of atoms

Formula mass = _____

5. $Mg(C_7H_5O_3)_2$

Element	Number of atoms	Atomic mass	Total mass of atoms

Formula mass = _____

WHAT DOES THE NUMBER IN FRONT MEAN?

Sometimes you see a compound or a symbol that has a number in front of it. What does this mean?

What does the 2 mean in 2Na or NaCl? What does the 3 mean in $3H_2$?

The number in front tells you how many atoms or molecules there are. You multiply each kind of atom by this number. The number in front is called a **coefficient** [koh-uh-FISH-unt]. Let's look at some examples:

2Na	2 Na means 2 atoms of sodium

2NaCl	2NaCl means two molecules of NaCl. That means two atoms of sodium and two atoms of chlorine.

$3H_2$	Here we must multiply the **3** × 2. There are 6 atoms of hydrogen.

$3H_2O$	There are still 6 atoms of hydrogen. but we also have oxygen. **3** × 1 = 3 atoms of oxygen.

Now let's see how to handle a compound that has both parentheses and a large number.

$2Ca(NO_3)_2$	The **2** means two molecules of $Ca(NO_3)_2$.

How many atoms of each element does this mean? We must multiply the number of each kind of atom by 2.

Ca   1 × 2 = 2 atoms

N   1   ×   ②   ×   ②   =   4 atoms

Subscript	Coefficient

O   3   ×   ②   ×   ②   =   12 atoms

An important thing to remember!

A coefficient in front of an element or a compound goes <u>only</u> with that element or compound. A plus (+) or an arrow (→) tells us where the value of the coefficient ends. For example:

$$4Fe + 3O_2 \quad \rightarrow \quad 2Fe_2O_3$$

- The 4 in front of the Fe goes only with the Fe.

- The 3 in front of the O_2 goes only with the O_2.

- But the 2 in front of Fe_2O_3 goes with the Fe_2 <u>and</u> the O_3. They are part of the same molecule.

LET'S JUST COUNT

Count the number of atoms in each of the following:

1. $2Ba(OH)_2$ Ba _____

              O _____

              H _____

2. $4Al_2(SO_4)_3$ Al _____

              S _____

              O _____

3. $3Ba(OH_2)$ Ba _____

              O _____

              H _____

4. $2Mg(C_7H_5O_3)_2$ Mg _____

              C _____

              H _____

              O _____

NOW BACK TO MASSES

Now you know how to handle formulas that have both parentheses and numbers in front. How do we figure masses for these formulas?

Simple, you have already learned that the formula mass of $Ca(NO_3)_2$ is 164. This means that one molecule has a mass of 164.

What is the mass of $2Ca(NO_3)_2$? Easy! Just multiply the formula mass by 2.

Mass of $2Ca(NO_3)_2$: $2 \times 164 =$ 328   =   FORMULA MASS

The formula mass of $Ba(OH)_2$ is 171. Figure the mass of each of the following:

1. $2Ba(OH)_2$ _____

2. $3Ba(OH)_2$ _____

The formula mass of $Pb(NO_3)_2$ is 331. Figure the mass of each of the following:

3. $2Pb(NO_3)_2$ _____

4. $4PB(NO_3)_2$ _____

REACHING OUT

1. Find the formula mass of this compound: $Fe(NH_4)_2 (SO_4)_2$.

_____

2. Find the mass of the following: $2Al_2(SO_3)_3$

_____

What is a chemical equation?

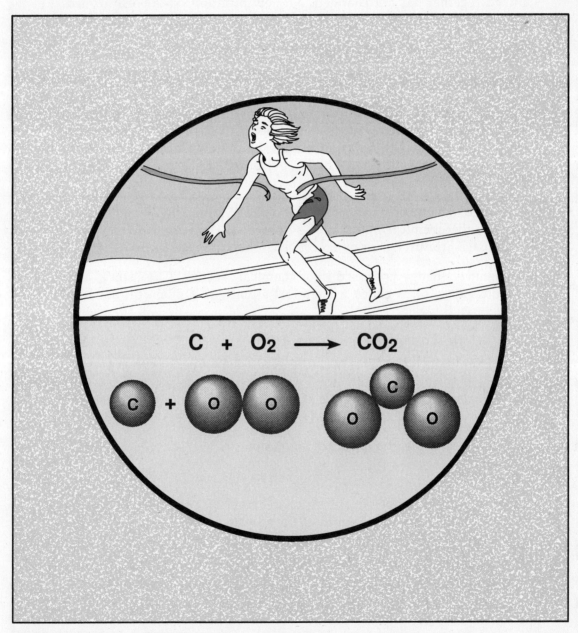

11

$$C + O_2 \longrightarrow CO_2$$

chemical change: change in matter that produces new products
chemical equation: set of symbols and formulas that describe a chemical change
physical change: change in matter that does not produce any new products
product: a substance that is produced in a chemical reaction (change)
reactant: substance that takes part in a chemical reaction (change)

LESSON 11 | What is a chemical equation?

You may tear a sheet of paper into tiny pieces, but you still have paper. Each piece is still paper no matter how small. The way the atoms are linked together has not changed. No new products have been formed. The properties of the paper have not changed. Neither has its formula.

A change like tearing paper is called a **physical change**. In a physical change, only the appearance of a substance changes. The chemical makeup does not change.

What happens when you burn paper? You no longer have paper. Paper is a compound made up mostly of carbon and hydrogen. When paper burns, it links up with oxygen from the air. Three products form—ash, water, and carbon dioxide. When paper burns, there is a change in the way atoms link together. New products form. Properties change.

A change like burning paper is called a **chemical change**. In a chemical change, the chemical makeup of a substance changes. New products form. Each product has its own properties. Each one has its own formula.

A chemical change is caused by a chemical reaction. The "story" of a chemical reaction is called a **chemical equation**. A chemical equation shows two things:

- which substance(s) we start out with

- which substance(s) we end up with

The substance or substances we <u>start out with</u> are called the **reactants**. The substance or substances we <u>end up with</u> are called the **products**.

This is an example of a chemical equation:

$$Fe + S \rightarrow FeS$$

This equation describes the chemical reaction that takes place when a mixture of iron (Fe) and sulfur (S) are heated. The Fe and S are the reactants. The FeS (iron sulfide) is the product. The arrow means "produces" or "yields."

The properties of iron sulfide are different from those of iron or sulfur.

Figure A *Sodium chloride (NaCl)*

Table salt (NaCl) is also called sodium chloride. It is a white solid. Your body contains this salt. It is necessary for life.

Figure B *Sodium (Na)*

Sodium (Na) is a very dangerous solid. It can explode in water.

Swallowing sodium can cause death.

Figure C *Chlorine (Cl)*

Chlorine (Cl) is a deadly greenish-yellow gas. If you inhale enough of this gas, it could be fatal.

Table salt can be melted. If an electric current passes through melted sodium chloride, a chemical reaction takes place. This is the chemical equation for this reaction.

$$2NaCl \rightarrow 2Na + Cl_2$$

67

Answer these questions.

1. This reaction has one reactant. Name that reactant. _____

2. The reactant in its natural state is a _____ .
   solid, liquid, gas

3. The reactant _____ dangerous.
   is, is not

4. Name the products. _____ _____

5. What is the state of sodium?_____

6. Is sodium dangerous? _____

7. Are the properties of sodium the same as the properties of sodium chloride?

   _____

8. What is the state of chlorine? _____

9. Is chlorine dangerous? _____

10. Are the properties of chlorine the same as the properties of sodium chloride?

    _____

11. In a chemical reaction, properties _____ change.
    do, do not

12. Name the kinds of atoms on the reactant side of this equation. _____

13. Name the kinds of atoms on the product side. _____ _____

14. The kinds of atoms on the reactant side _____ the same as the atoms
    on the resultant side.   are, are not

15. Are they in the same form? _____

16. The atoms in the reactant are part of_____ .
    a compound, two elements

17. The atoms in the product are part of_____ .
    a compound, two elements

18. The arrangements of the atoms_____ changed.
    has, has not

19. In this reaction, atoms have _____ .
    separated, linked up

20. In a chemical reaction, the arrangement of the elements _____ change.
    does, does not

PRODUCT OR REACTANT?

Five chemical equations are given below. Below each equation you will find the name of each substance in this equation. For each chemical equation:

- Write reactant next to each substance that is a reactant.

- Write product next to each substance that is a product.

1. $Zn + FeSO4 \rightarrow ZnSO4 + Fe$

   Zinc sulfate _____   Iron _____

   Zinc _____   Iron sulfate _____

2. $4HCl + MnO_2 \rightarrow MnCl2 + 2H_2O + Cl_2$

   Chlorine _____

   Manganese chloride _____

   Manganese dioxide _____

   Water _____

   Hydrochloric acid (Hydrogen chloride) _____

3. $H_2SO_4 + BaCl_2 \rightarrow 2HCl + BaSO_4$

   Barium chloride _____

   Hydrochloric acid (hydrogen chloride) _____

   Barium sulfate _____

   Sulfuric acid (hydrogen sulfate) _____

4. $Br_2 + 2KI \rightarrow 2KBr + I_2$

   Potassium bromide _____   Iodine _____

   Bromine _____   Potassium iodide _____

5. $2ZnS + 3O_2 \rightarrow 2ZnO + 2SO_2$

   Oxygen _____   Sulfur dioxide _____

   Zinc oxide _____   Zinc sulfide _____

FILL IN THE BLANK

Complete each statement using a term or terms from the list below. Write your answers in the spaces provided.

products	right	physical
chemical equation	take part	yields
new	chemical	reaction
arrow	reactants	left

1. A change in which no new products are formed is called a _____ change.

2. A change in which new products are formed is called a _____ change.

3. Another way of saying "chemical change" is "chemical _____."

4. A set of symbols and formulas that describes a chemical reaction is called a

    _____.

5. A chemical equation tells which substances _____ in a chemical

    reaction. It also tells which _____ substances are formed.

6. The substances that take part in a chemical reaction are called the

    _____.

7. The new substances that form in a chemical reaction are called the

    _____.

8. In a chemical equation, the reactants are on the _____ side. The

    products are on the _____ side.

9. In a chemical reaction, the reactants and products are separated by an

    _____.

10. The arrow means "produces" or "_____".

REACHING OUT

Sodium hydroxide reacts with hydrochloric acid (hydrogen chloride) to produce sodium chloride (table salt) and water. Write the equation that shows this reaction.

How do you balance a chemical equation?

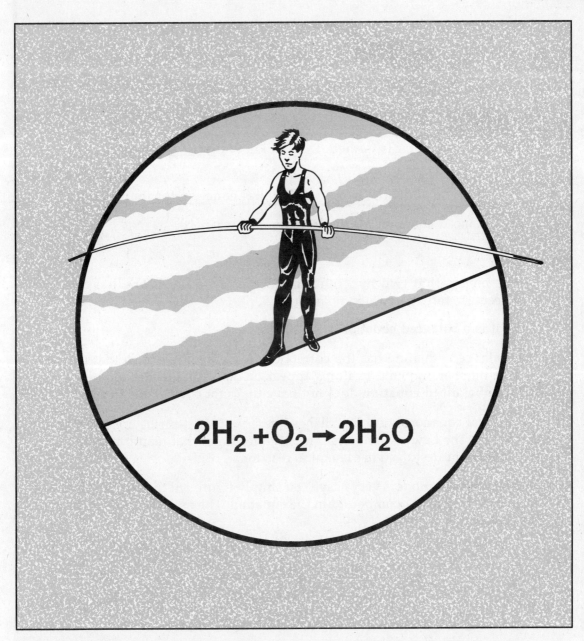

12

$$2H_2 + O_2 \rightarrow 2H_2O$$

balanced equation: description of a reaction that obeys the *Law of Conservation of Matter* so that the kind and number of atoms on both sides of the equation is equal

unbalanced equation: description of a reaction that does not obey the *Law of Conservation of Matter*

LESSON 12 | How do you balance a chemical equation?

You know that hydrogen reacts with oxygen to form water, but do you know <u>how many atoms</u> of hydrogen react with <u>how many atoms</u> of oxygen when water is formed. Do you know <u>how many molecules</u> of water are formed?

You do if you know the balanced chemical equation for the reaction.

The balanced equation for the formation of water is:

$$2\,H_2 \quad + \quad O_2 \qquad \rightarrow \qquad 2\,H_2O$$

This means that two hydrogen molecules react with one oxygen molecule to form two water molecules.

What is a balanced equation?

A **balanced equation** has the correct coeffeicients in place so that the same number and kind of atoms appear on both sides of the equation. An **unbalanced equation** does not have the right coefficients in place.

Chemical equations must be balanced because they describe a chemical reaction. The Law of Conservation of Matter states that matter may not be created or destroyed in a chemical reaction.

Balancing equations is very easy. You simply figure out the coefficients for each element or compound in the equation. The next few pages will show you how.

HOW TO BALANCE A CHEMICAL EQUATION

First of all, be certain that the formulas for the compounds are correct. You cannot just "make up" a chemical reaction.

It is possible that the equation is already balanced. Do you have the same number of atoms of each element - on both sides of the equation? If you do, then you do nothing more. Your work is already done. However, if the equation is not balanced, then you must balance it.

For example carbon and oxygen combine to form carbon dioxide.

$$C \quad + \quad O_2 \quad \rightarrow \quad CO_2$$

In this equation:

- one atom of carbon (C) is on the left side
- one atom of carbon (C) is on the right side
- two atoms of oxygen (O) is on the left side
- two atoms of oxygen (O) is on the right side

The equation is balanced.

However, when lithium and sulfur form lithium sulfide, things are not quite so easy.

The unbalanced equation is:

$$Li \quad + \quad S \quad \rightarrow \quad Li_2S$$

In this equation:

- one atom of lithium (Li) is on the left side
- two atoms of (Li) are on the right side
- one atom of sulfur (S) is on the left side
- one atom of sulfur (S) is on the right side

This equation is not balanced. There is only one atom of lithium (Li) on the left side and there are two atoms of lithium (Li) on the right side.

To balance the equation, there must be two atoms of lithium on the left side of the equation. A coefficient of "2" is put in front of Li on the left side of the equation.

$$2\,Li \quad + \quad S \quad \rightarrow \quad Li_2S$$

Now there are two atoms of lithium (Li) on each side of the equation. The equation is balanced.

BALANCED OR UNBALANCED

Ten equations are listed below. Some are balanced and some are unbalanced. Make a check (✓) in the correct box next to each equation.

	Equation	Balanced	Unbalanced
1.	$Fe + S \rightarrow FeS$		
2.	$Mg + O_2 \rightarrow MgO$		
3.	$C + O_2 \rightarrow CO_2$		
4.	$P_4 + O_2 \rightarrow P_4O_{10}$		
5.	$H_2 + O_2 \rightarrow H_2O$		
6.	$Na + O_2 \rightarrow NaO_2$		
7.	$CuO + H_2 \rightarrow Cu + H_2O$		
8.	$Cu + S \rightarrow Cu_2S$		
9.	$Zn + 2\,HCl \rightarrow ZnCl_2 + H_2$		
10.	$2\,Na + H_2O \rightarrow 2\,NaOH + H_2$		

MATCHING

Match each term in Column A with its description in Column B. Write the correct letter in the space provided.

Column A

_____ 1. coefficient

_____ 2. subscript

_____ 3. balanced equation

_____ 4. unbalanced equation

_____ 5. Law of Conservation of Matter

Column B

a) states that matter cannot be created or destroyed

b) small number after a symbol

c) does not obey the Law of Conservation of Matter

d) number in front of a compound

e) same kind and number of atoms on both sides of the equation

BALANCING AN EQUATION

Calcium and Oxygen combine to form Calcium Carbonate. A students first attempt at balancing this equation is shown below. Look at the equation and answer the questions below.

$$Ca \quad + \quad O_2 \quad \rightarrow \quad CaO$$

In this equation:

1. How many atoms of Calcium (Ca) are there on the left side? _____

2. How many atoms of Calcium (Ca) are there on the right side? _____

3. How many atoms of Oxygen (O) are there on the left side? _____

4. How many atoms of Oxygen (O) are there on the right side? _____

5. Are there the same number of Calcium atoms on both sides? _____

6. Are there the same number of Oxygen atoms on both sides? _____

7. Is this equation balanced? _____

The student's second attempt at balancing this equation is shown below. Look at the equation and answer the questions.

$$Ca \quad + \quad O_2 \quad \rightarrow \quad 2\,CaO$$

In this equation:

1. How many atoms of Calcium (Ca) are there on the left side? _____

2. How many atoms of Calcium (Ca) are there on the right side? _____

3. How many atoms of Oxygen (O) are there on the left side? _____

4. How many atoms of Oxygen (O) are there on the right side? _____

5. Are there the same number of Calcium atoms on both sides? _____

6. Are there the same number of Oxygen atoms on both sides? _____

7. Is this equation balanced? _____

The student's third attempt at balancing this equation is shown below. Look at the equation and answer the questions.

$$2\ Ca\ +\ O_2\ \rightarrow\ 2\ CaO$$

In this equation:

1. How many atoms of Calcium (Ca) are there on the left side? _____

2. How many atoms of Calcium (Ca) are there on the right side? _____

3. How many atoms of Oxygen (O) are there on the left side? _____

4. How many atoms of Oxygen (O) are there on the right side? _____

5. Are there the same number of Calcium atoms on both sides? _____

6. Are there the same number of Oxygen atoms on both sides? _____

7. Is this equation balanced? _____

BALANCING AN EQUATION ON YOUR OWN

Balance the equations below by filling in the blanks below. The first one is done for you.

1. __2__ Cu + __1__ S → __1__ Cu_2S

2. _____ Li + _____ Fl_2 → _____ LiFl

3. _____ Na + _____ Cl_2 → _____ NaCl

4. _____ P_4 + _____ O_2 → _____ P_4O_{10}

5. _____ Na + _____ H_2O → _____ NaOH + _____ H_2

Does a chemical reaction destroy matter?

13

Law of Conservation of Matter: scientific statement that says that a chemical reaction does not destroy or create matter.

LESSON 13 | Does a chemical reaction destroy matter?

In a chemical reaction, atoms change the way they are linked together. New products form. But are any atoms lost during the changeover? Is any matter destroyed?

The burning of wood and rusting are two examples of chemical reactions.

- Wood burns, and a small amount of ash remains behind.

- A car rusts, and it looks like it's wearing away.

It surely seems that some matter is lost. But is it really? This is how we can find out:

1. Find the mass of the reactants. That means find the mass of <u>all</u> the substances that take part in a chemical reaction.

2. Then find the mass of the products. That means find the mass of <u>all</u> the new substances that form.

If there is a loss of mass, then we know that some matter was destroyed.

If there is no loss of mass, then we know that matter was not destroyed.

In any chemical reaction, there is no mass loss. The mass of the products is the same as the mass of the reactants. In other words, we end up with the same mass as we started with. This means that no matter was destroyed.

In a chemical reaction, matter is not destroyed. This is part of a scientific statement called the **Law of Conservation of Matter**.

Can matter be destroyed? Yes! But not in a chemical reaction. It takes an atomic or nuclear reaction to destroy matter. When matter is destroyed, it changes into energy. This is the idea behind atomic energy.

UNDERSTANDING CONSERVATION OF MATTER

Look at Figures A and B. Then answer the questions.

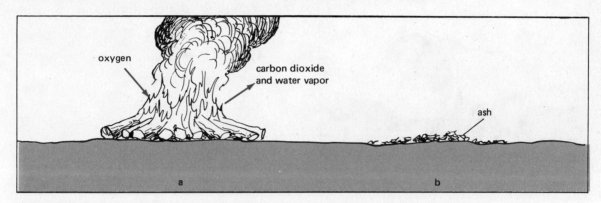

Figure A

Wood, like paper, is made up mostly of carbon and hydrogen.

When wood burns, it links up with oxygen. The reaction produces ash, carbon dioxide, and water vapor. (Heat energy is also produced. But energy has no mass.)

Wood + Oxygen → Ash + Carbon dioxide + Water vapor

1. Name the reactants when wood burns. _____

2. Name the products. _____

3. Where does the oxygen come from? _____

4. The ash remains behind. What happens to the carbon dioxide and water? _____

   _____

5. If the reactants have a mass of 10 kilograms, what will the mass of the products be?

   _____

6. Is any matter lost? _____

7. Is matter lost during any chemical reaction? _____

8. In a chemical reaction, the mass of the products equals the mass of the

   _____ . In other words, "the mass you start with is the mass you

   _____ ."

9. Name the scientific statement that tells us that matter is not destroyed during a

   chemical reaction. _____

THE RUSTING OF IRON

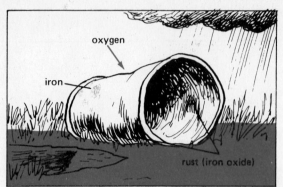

When iron rusts, it links up with oxygen. This is the formula for the reaction:

$$4Fe + 3O_2 \rightarrow 2Fe_2O_3$$

Iron   Oxygen   Iron oxide
(Rust)

Figure B

1. Name the reactants. _____ _____

2. Where did the oxygen come from? _____

3. What is the chemical name of the product? _____

4. What is the common name of the product? _____

Look at the equation. Answer the questions.

5. How many atoms of iron did we start with? _____

6. The atomic mass of iron is 56. What is the mass of all the iron atoms? _____

7. How many atoms of oxygen did we start with? _____

8. The atomic mass of oxygen is 16. What is the mass of all the oxygen atoms?

   _____

9. Altogether, what is the mass of the reactants? _____

10. How many atoms of iron did we end with? _____

11. What is the mass of all these atoms? _____

12. How many atoms of oxygen did we end with? _____

13. What is the mass of all these atoms? _____

14. Altogether, what is the mass of the product? _____

15. Is the mass of the product the same as the mass of the reactants? _____

16. Was any matter lost? _____

17. How do you know? _____

18. Is any matter destroyed in a chemical reaction? _____

19. What happens to atoms during a chemical reaction? _____

_____

20. The equation for rusting is a "balanced" equation. What do you think this means?

_____

_____

COUNTING ATOMS

Let's work with the equation in a different way. This time let's just count atoms.

$$4Fe + 3O_2 \rightarrow 2Fe_2O_3$$

1. Name the kinds of atoms of the reactant side of the equation. _____

_____

2. Name the kinds of atoms on the product side. _____ _____

3. The kinds of atom on the product side _____ the same as the
   kinds of atoms on the reactant side.   are, are not

4. How many atoms of iron are there on the reactant side? _____

5. How many atoms of iron are there on the product side? _____

6. How many atoms of oxygen are there on the reactant side? _____

7. How many atoms of oxygen are there on the product side? _____

8. The number of any kind of atom _____ the same on both sides of
   the equation.   is, is not

9. If the number of each kind of atom is the same on both sides of the equation,

   then what else is equal? _____

10. This shows that matter _____ destroyed.
                              was, was not

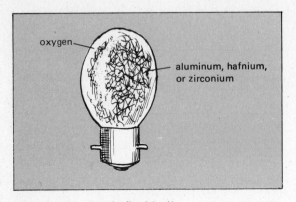

Figure C   *Fresh flashbulb*

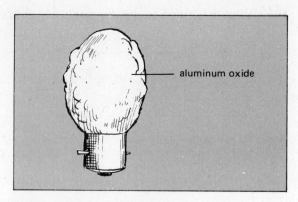

Figure D   *Used flashbulb*

What You Need to Know (Background Information)

Everyone knows what a flashbulb is. It gives off a bright flash of light. It lets us take pictures where there is little light.

A flashbulb contains oxygen and shreds of metal like aluminum, hafnium, or zirconium.

When a bulb "goes off," a chemical reaction takes place. The oxygen links up with the metal. This produces an oxide of the metal. For example, if the bulb contains aluminum, aluminum oxide forms.

This is the equation for the reaction:

$$4AL + 3O_2 \rightarrow 2Al_2O_3 \text{ (+ Light + Heat)}$$

What You Need (Materials)

balance scale   heat proof pad
6 volt battery   two insulated wires
fireproof cloth   a flashbulb

What To Do (Procedure)

1. Find the mass of the bulb before you flash it. What is the mass of the bulb?

   _____ grams

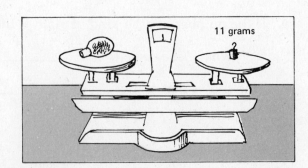

Figure E

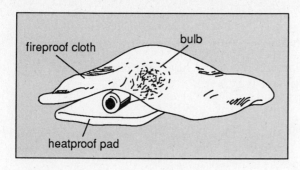

Figure F

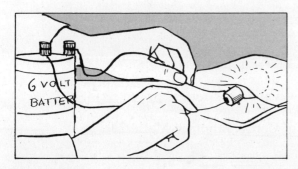

Figure G

Figure H

2. Place the bulb on the heat proof pad. Cover most of the bulb with the fireproof cloth. Keep only the end of the metal base uncovered. (Figure F)

3. Flash the bulb. (Figure G)

4. Uncover the bulb. Wait about one minute until it cools. Then weigh it again. (Figure H)

What is the mass of the bulb now?

_____ grams

What You Learned (Observations)

1. What was the mass of the bulb before it was flashed? _____

2. What was the mass of the bulb after it was flashed? _____

3. A flashbulb "going off" causes a

_____ change.
     physical, chemical

4. If a chemical reaction destroys matter, than the bulb would become

_____ .
     heavier, lighter

5. Did the bulb become lighter after it was flashed? _____

Something To Think About (Conclusions)

1. Matter _____ destroyed.
        was, was not

2. A chemical reaction _____ destroy matter.
             does, does not

BALANCED OR NOT BALANCED?

Four equations are listed below. Two are balanced. Two are not. Figure out which ones are balanced. (Hint: Counting atoms is the easiest way.)

Equations

A. $Zn + H_2SO_4 \longrightarrow ZnSO_4 + H_2$

B. $Mg + O_2 \rightarrow 2MgO$

C. $Na_2S + 2HCl \rightarrow 2NaCl + H_2S$

D. $H_2S + SO_2 \rightarrow 3S + 2H_2O$

1. Which equations are balanced? _____

2. Which equations are not balanced? _____

3. Which equations show the Law of Conservation of Matter? _____

4. Which equations do not show the Law of Conservation of Matter? _____

5. Which equations are not possible? _____

REACHING OUT

Figure I *Uranium fuel*

A nuclear reaction destroys matter. Nuclear fuel, like uranium, changes to energy.

How can we show that matter is lost in a nuclear reaction? (Hint: Look back at the flashbulb experiment.)

_____

_____

_____

_____

_____

What is a synthesis reaction?

14

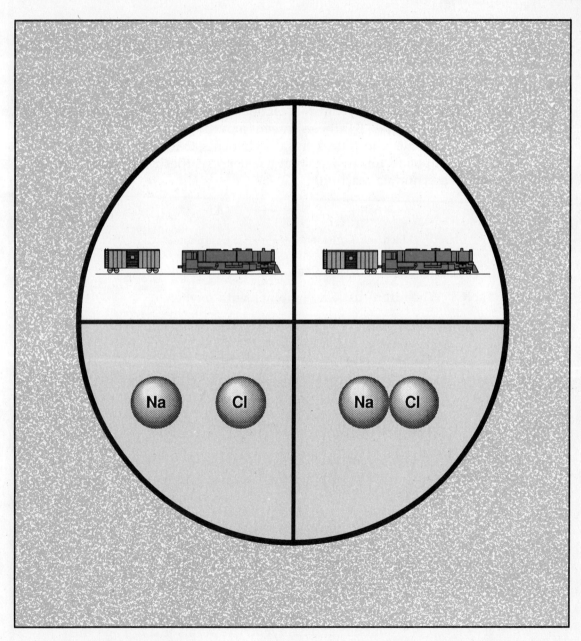

synthesis [SIN-thuh-sis] **reaction:** combining of several substances to form a more complicated substance

LESSON 14 | What is a synthesis reaction?

Chemical reactions are happening around you all the time. A match burns. A car rusts. food spoils. Leaves decay. These are just a few chemical reactions.

Probably the most important chemical reactions take place in your body. They are happening this very moment. Digestion is a chemical process. So is respiration. In every one of your trillions of cells, chemical reactions are taking place all the time. Life depends upon chemical reactions.

There are several kinds of chemical reactions. One kind is the **synthesis** [SIN-thuh-sis] **reaction.** "Synthesis" means a putting together. A synthesis reaction combines substances, usually elements, to form a compound. When the compound forms, we say it has been synthesized. Below is a "model" of a synthesis reaction.

$$A + B \longrightarrow AB$$

$$\text{Element} + \text{Element} \longrightarrow \text{Compound}$$

Let's study two synthesis reactions.

RUSTING When iron rusts, it <u>combines</u> with oxygen.

Remember this equation?

$$4Fe + 3O_2 \longrightarrow 2Fe_2O_3$$

$$\text{Iron} + \text{Oxygen} \longrightarrow \text{Iron oxide (rust)}$$

$$\text{Element} + \text{Element} \xrightarrow[\text{to form}]{\text{link up}} \text{Compound}$$

THE BURNING OF CARBON Charcoal is made of the element carbon (C). When carbon burns, it <u>combines</u> with oxygen. This produces the gas carbon dioxide (CO_2).

$$C + O_2 \longrightarrow CO_2$$

$$\text{Carbon} + \text{Oxygen} \xrightarrow[\text{to form}]{\text{link up}} \text{Carbon dioxide}$$

$$\text{Element} + \text{Element} \longrightarrow \text{Compound}$$

A synthesis reaction is like any other kind of chemical reaction. No matter is created. No matter is destroyed. The atoms just change their arrangement.

UNDERSTANDING SYNTHESIS REACTIONS

Look at Figures A through E and read the explanation. Then answer the questions with each.

When hydrogen explodes, it combines with oxygen. Water is produced. This equation shows what happens:

$$H_2 + O_2 \longrightarrow H_2O$$

Hydrogen + Oxygen $\longrightarrow$ Water

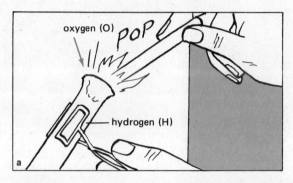

Figure A

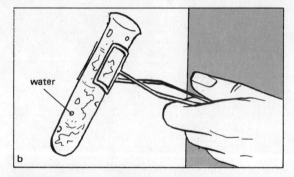

Figure B

1. Hydrogen is_____ .
   an element, a compound

2. Oxygen is _____ .
   an element, a compound

3. Water is _____ .
   an element, a compound

4. Is the formation of water a synthesis reaction? _____

5. Why is the formation of water a synthesis reaction? _____

   _____

   _____

When powdered sulfur and iron filings are heated together, they form iron sulfide.

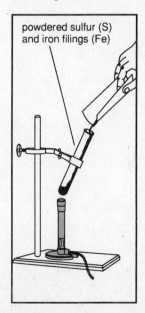

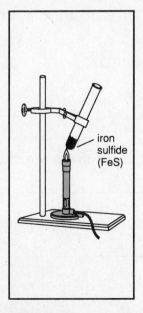

Figure C   **Figure D**

This equation shows what happens:

$$Fe + S \longrightarrow FeS$$

Iron + Sulfur $\longrightarrow$ Iron sulfide

1. Iron is _____ .
   an element, a compound

2. Sulfur is _____ .
   an element, a compound

3. Iron sulfide is _____ .
   an element, a compound

4. What happens to the iron and sulfur when they form iron sulfide? _____

   _____

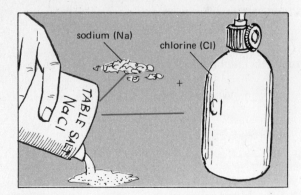

Figure E

Sodium combines with chlorine to form sodium chloride—common table salt.

This equation shows what happens:

$$Na \quad + \quad Cl \quad \longrightarrow \quad NaCl$$

Sodium + Chlorine $\longrightarrow$ Sodium chloride

1. Sodium is _____ .
   <u>an element, a compound</u>

2. Chlorine is _____ .
   <u>an element, a compound</u>

3. Sodium chloride is _____ .
   <u>an element, a compound</u>

4. What kind of reaction is the formation of sodium chloride? _____

   Why? _____

YOUR OWN WORDS, PLEASE

1. What does "synthesis" mean? _____

   _____

2. What does "synthesis reaction" mean? _____

   _____

Two synthesis equations are shown below. They are different from the ones you have already seen.

Equation I $CO_2 + C \quad \longrightarrow \quad 2CO_2$

Equation II $CO_2 + H_2O \quad \longrightarrow \quad H_2CO_3$

3. How is Equation I different from the other synthesis equations in this lesson?

   _____

4. How is Equation II different from the other synthesis equations in this lesson?

   _____

IDENTIFYING SYNTHESIS REACTIONS

Ten equations are listed below. Some are synthesis reactions. Some are not. Make a check (✓) in the correct box next to each equation.

	Equation	A Synthesis Reaction	Not a Synthesis Reaction
1.	$2K + Br_2 \longrightarrow 2KBr$		
2.	$2H_2O \longrightarrow 2H_2 + O_2$		
3.	$NaCl \longrightarrow Na + Cl$		
4.	$4Au + 3O_2 \longrightarrow 2Au_2O_3$		
5.	$2Na + 2HCl \longrightarrow 2NaCl + H_2$		
6.	$Cu + Br_2 \longrightarrow CuBr_2$		
7.	$Zn + S \longrightarrow ZnS$		
8.	$2NA + Br_2 \longrightarrow 2NaBr$		
9.	$2HgO \longrightarrow 2Hg + O_2$		
10.	$2Na + I_2 \longrightarrow 2NaI$		

TRUE OR FALSE

In the space provided, write "true" if the sentence is true. Write "false" if the sentence is false.

_____ 1. There is only one kind of chemical reaction.

_____ 2. A synthesis reaction separates a compound into its elements.

_____ 3. The reactants of every synthesis reaction are elements.

_____ 4. The product of a synthesis reaction is a compound.

_____ 5. Chemical reactions take place only in the laboratory.

WORD SEARCH

The list on the left contains words that you have used in this Lesson. Find and circle each word where it appears. in the box. the spellings may go in any direction: up, down, left, right, or diagonally.

MATTER

POLYVALENT

RADICAL

MASS

REACTANT

FORMULA

PHYSICAL

PRODUCT

YIELDS

CHEMICAL

C	T	L	A	C	I	S	Y	H	P	A
H	O	N	L	A	C	I	M	E	H	C
I	Y	I	E	L	D	S	C	N	O	D
M	M	C	A	L	U	M	R	O	F	M
T	N	A	T	C	A	E	R	T	T	Y
N	E	L	S	H	W	V	H	G	C	L
R	I	A	L	S	S	A	Y	L	U	L
A	L	R	A	D	I	C	A	L	D	I
I	S	Y	R	A	G	L	E	Y	O	M
J	E	R	R	R	H	D	W	I	R	P
C	L	R	E	T	T	A	M	E	P	I

REACHING OUT

Most compounds made of only two elements have names ending in *-ide*. For example:

NaCl = sodium chloride

K_2S = potassium sulfide

Can you name these compounds?

	Formula	Name
1.	CaO	
2.	KI	
3.	NaBr	
4.	AgF	
5.	MgCl	

What is a decomposition reaction?

15

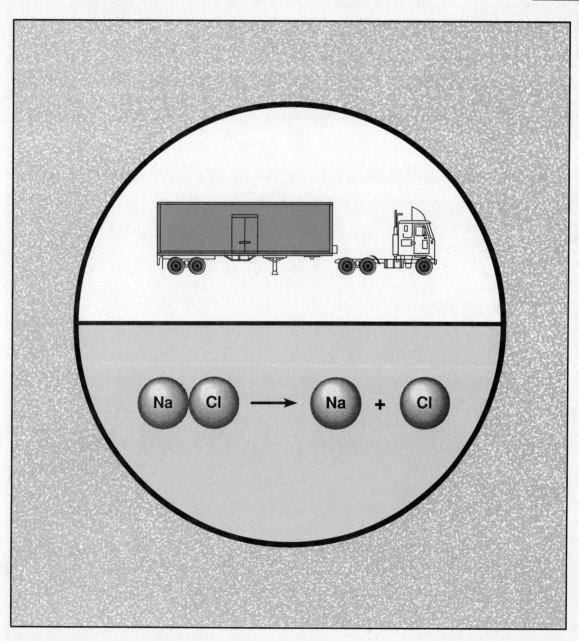

decomposition [dee-kahm-puh-ZISH-un]: breakdown of a substance into simpler substances

electrolysis [i-lek-TRAHL-uh-sis]: decomposition of a substance by means of electricity

LESSON 15 | What is a decomposition reaction?

Synthesis reactions build compounds. Anything that can be built can also be taken apart. The breakdown of a compound into simpler substances is called **decomposition** [dee-kahm-puh-ZISH-un]. Decomposition is a chemical process.

Let us look at two examples.

1. Common table salt (sodium chloride) is a compound. It is composed of the elements sodium and chlorine.

Sodium chloride can be melted. If electricity is passed through melted sodium chloride, it decomposes. The molecules unlock. They change back to atoms of sodium and chlorine. This equation shows the reaction:

$$2NaCl \xrightarrow[\text{into}]{\text{breaks down}} 2Na + Cl_2$$

Sodium chloride	Sodium	Chlorine
(compound)	(element)	(element)

The decomposition of a compound by means of electricity is called **electrolysis** [i-lek-TRAHL-uh-sis]. Only certain compounds can be decomposed by electrolysis. Usually these compounds are liquids.

2. Potassium chlorate ($KClO_3$) is a compound. It is composed of the elements potassium, chlorine, and oxygen.

Heat decomposes potassium chlorate. Potassium chlorate changes to oxygen and potassium chloride (a simpler compound). This equation shows the reaction:

$$2KClO_3 \longrightarrow 2KCl + 3O_2$$

Potassium chlorate	Potassium Chloride	Oxygen
(compound)	(a simpler compound)	(element)

Notice that the decomposition is not complete. The oxygen has been separated. But the potassium and chlorine are still joined to form the compound potassium chloride. Another kind of decomposition reaction can separate potassium chloride into its elements.

Only certain compounds are decomposed with heat.

UNDERSTANDING DECOMPOSITION REACTIONS

Look at Figure A. Then answer the questions or fill in the blanks.

Electrolysis decomposes water. This is the equation for the reaction:

$$2H_2O \longrightarrow 2H_2 + O_2$$

Water   Hydrogen + Oxygen

1. What is the formula for water? _____

2. Water is _____ .
   <small>an element, a compound</small>

3. Name the elements that make up water.

   _____

4. Name the process that decomposes water.

   _____

5. What kind of energy is used?

   _____

6. When water decomposes. It changes to the

   elements _____ and

   _____ .

7. Water is in the _____ state.
   <small>solid, liquid, gas</small>

8. Hydrogen is in the _____ state.
   <small>solid, liquid, gas</small>

9. Oxygen is in the _____ state.
   <small>solid, liquid, gas</small>

10. Which is simpler, water or the elements that make up water? _____

    _____

11. Decomposition _____ compounds.
    <small>builds up, breaks down</small>

12. Can electrolysis decompose every compound? _____

13. Name another compound that can be decomposed with electrolysis.

    _____

14. A compound that can be separated by electrolysis must be in which state of matter?

    _____

water
(H₂O)

oxygen (O)

hydrogen (H)

6 volt
battery

Figure A

Look at Figure B. Answer the questions.

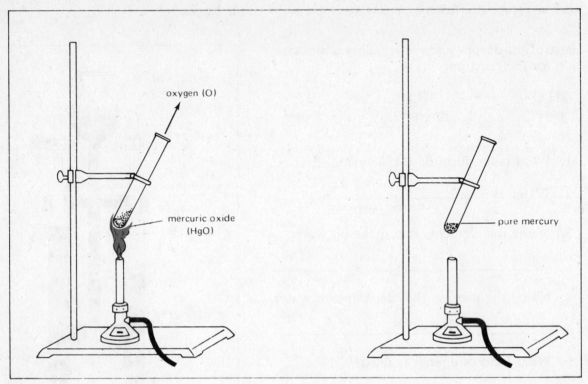

Figure B

Mercuric oxide is a solid. Heat decomposes mercuric oxide. This is the equation for the reaction.

$$2HgO \xrightarrow{\text{heat}} 2Hg \quad + \quad O_2$$

Mercuric oxide   Mercury   +   Oxygen

1. What is the formula for mercuric oxide? _____

2. Mercuric oxide is _____ .
   _{an element, a compound}

3. Name the elements that make up mercuric oxide. _____

   _____

4. What happens when mercuric oxide is heated? _____

5. What kind of energy decomposes mercuric oxide? _____

6. When mercuric oxide decomposes, it changes to the elements_____ and

   _____ .

7. Mercuric oxide is in the _____ state.
   _{solid, liquid, gas}

94

8. Mercury is in the _____ state.
                                     solid, liquid, gas

9. Oxygen is in the _____ state.
                               solid, liquid, gas

10. Which is simpler: mercuric oxide or the elements that make up mercuric oxide?

_____

11. The mercury _____ .
                         stays in the test tube, escapes into the air

12. The oxygen _____ .
                       stays in the test tube, escapes into the air

13. Can heat decompose every compound? _____

14. Name another compound that can be decomposed by heat. _____

FILL IN THE BLANK

Complete each statement using a term or terms from the list below. Write your answers in the spaces provided.

    heating   mercuric oxide   electrolysis
    Potassium chlorate   synthesis   molten sodium chloride
    liquid   fewer   decomposition
    simpler   water

1. The combining of substances to form a compound is called _____ .

2. The breakdown of a compound into simpler substances is called

_____ .

3. Two methods used to decompose compounds are _____ and

_____ .

4. For a compound to decompose by electrolysis, it must be in a _____ state.

5. Two compounds that can be decomposed by electrolysis are

_____ and _____ .

6. Two compounds that can be decomposed by heat are _____

and _____ .

7. Atoms are _____ than molecules.

8. KCl is a simpler compound than $KClO_3$ because KCl has _____ elements and atoms.

MATCHING

Match each term in Column A with its description in Column B. Write the correct letter in the space provided.

Column A	Column B
_____ 1. synthesis reaction	a) breaks down compounds
_____ 2. decomposition reaction	b) uses electricity
_____ 3. electrolysis and heat	c) methods of decomposition
_____ 4. electrolysis	d) simpler than a compound
_____ 5. an element	e) builds compounds

IDENTIFYING DECOMPOSITION REACTIONS

Ten chemical equations are listed below. Some are decomposition reactions. Some are not. Mark a (✔) in the correct box next to each equation.

	Equation	Decomposition Reaction	Not a Decomposition Reaction
1.	$CuCl_2 \rightarrow Cu + Cl_2$		
2.	$3Hf + 2N_2 \rightarrow Hf_3N_4$		
3.	$Zn + 2HCl \rightarrow ZnCl_2 + H_2$		
4.	$H_2CO_3 \rightarrow H_2O + CO_2$		
5.	$2NaOH \rightarrow 2Na + O_2 + H_2$		
6.	$Fe + S \rightarrow FeS$		
7.	$CaCO_3 \rightarrow CaO + CO_2$		
8.	$4P + 5O_2 \rightarrow 2P_2O_5$		
9.	$C + O_2 \rightarrow CO_2$		
10.	$Ca(OH)_2 \rightarrow CaO + H_2O$		

REACHING OUT

1. Does boiling decompose water? _____

2. What does boiling do to water? _____

_____

What is a replacement reaction?

16

replacement reaction: reaction in which one kind of matter replaces another kind

LESSON 16 | What is a replacement reaction?

Imagine that three children are playing.

Two are holding hands. The other is alone.

The child that was alone now joins the others. He takes the place of one of the children.

Now a different child is alone.

We have the same children that we started with. But, now they are arranged in a different way.

Some chemical reactions work like this. A free element takes the place of or replaces another element of a compound.

The element that was replaced is now "free."

$$A \quad + \quad BC \quad \longrightarrow \quad AC \quad + \quad B$$
free element   compound   new compound   new free element

Let's study an actual replacement reaction—one between zinc (Zn) and hydrochloric acid (HCl).

The zinc is the "free" element. The hydrochloric acid is in the compound.

$$Zn \quad + \quad 2HCl \quad \longrightarrow \quad ZnCl_2 \quad + \quad H_2$$
The zinc replaces the hydrogen.   The hydrogen is set free.

The reaction produces a new compound, zinc chloride ($ZnCl_2$), and free hydrogen (H_2). Notice that the elements we started with are the elements we ended with. They are just arranged in a different way.

This kind of reaction is called a single replacement reaction. In a single replacement reaction, a free element replaces a different element of a compound.

UNDERSTANDING SINGLE REPLACEMENT REACTIONS

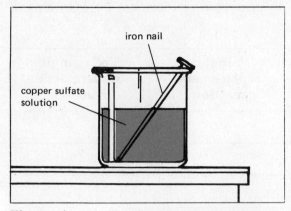

iron nail

copper sulfate solution

Figure A

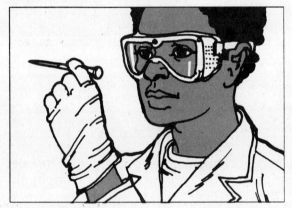

Figure B

What You Need (Materials)

iron nail
copper sulfate solution
beaker

How To Do The Experiment (Procedure)

Place an iron nail in copper sulfate solution.

Remove the nail in a few minutes.

What You Saw (Observations)

The nail is coated with copper.

This is the equation for the reaction.

$$Fe + CuSO_4 \rightarrow FeSO_4 + Cu$$

Iron   Copper sulfate   Iron sulfate   Copper

1. Name the free element we started with. _____

2. Name the compound we started with. _____

3. Name the free element we ended with. _____

4. Name the compound we ended with. _____

5. **a)** Which element did the iron replace? _____

   b) What happened to this element? _____

6. What do we call this kind of chemical reaction? _____

7. What happens during a single replacement reaction? _____

_____

IDENTIFYING SINGLE REPLACEMENT REACTIONS

Six equations are listed below. Some are single replacement reactions. Some are not. Mark a check (✓) in the correct box next to each equation.

	Equation	Single replacement reaction	Not a single replacement reaction
1.	$C + 2S \rightarrow CS_2$		
2.	$H_2O_2 \rightarrow H_2 + O_2$		
3.	$2Al + 6HCl \rightarrow 2AlCl_3 + 3H_2$		
4.	$2K + Cl_2 \rightarrow 2KCl$		
5.	$Zn + PbO \rightarrow ZnO + Pb$		
6.	$Fe + CuSO_4 \rightarrow FeSO_4 + Cu$		

DOUBLE REPLACEMENT REACTIONS

A <u>single</u> replacement reaction takes place between an element and a compound. The free element replaces one of the elements of the compound. This produces a new compound and a new free element.

$$A \quad + \quad BC \quad \rightarrow \quad AC \quad + \quad B$$

free element   compound   new compound   new free element

A <u>double</u> replacement reaction takes place between <u>two</u> compounds. A part of one compound changes place with a part of the other compound.

Let us use playing children as models again to see what happens.

Children A and B stand for compound AB.
Children C and D stand for compound CD.

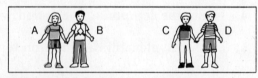

Figure C

Child A changes place with child C.

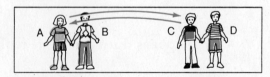

Figure D

What do we have now? Instead of compounds AB and CD, we have two new compounds—CB and AD.

When there are two changeovers, a double replacement has taken place.

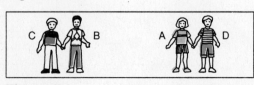

Figure E

New let us study an actual double replacement reaction—the reaction between sodium hydroxide (NaOH), and hydrochloric acid (HCl).

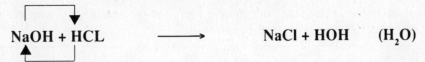

NaOH + HCL $\longrightarrow$ NaCl + HOH   (H$_2$O)

- The sodium and hydrogen change places.
- Two new compounds form—NaCl (common table salt) and HOH (water).

Now you try. Read each equation carefully. Then answer the questions or fill in the blanks with each.

Equation I   BaCl$_2$ +   Na$_2$SO$_4$ →   BaSO$_4$ +   2NaCl
              Barium chloride   Sodium sulfate   Barium sulfate   Sodium chloride

1. Name the reactants. _____ _____

2. The reactants are _____ .
   both elements, both compounds, an element and a compound

3. The barium changed places with the _____ .
   sulfate, chlorine, sodium

4. Name the products. _____ _____

5. The products are _____ .
   both elements, both compounds, an element and a compound

6. What kind of chemical reaction is this? _____

7. Double replacement is the reaction of two _____ to form two new

   _____ .

Equation II   AgNO$_3$ +   NaBr   →   AgBr   +   NaNO$_3$
              Silver nitrate   Sodium bromide   Silver bromide   Sodium nitrate

8. Name the reactants. _____ _____

9. The reactants are _____ .
   both elements, both compounds, an element and a compound

10. The silver changed places with the _____ .
    sodium, bromine, nitrate

11. Name the products. _____ _____

12. The products are _____ .
    both elements, both compounds, an element and a compound

13. What kind of chemical reaction is this? _____

IDENTIFYING DOUBLE REPLACEMENT REACTIONS

Eight equations are listed below. Some are double replacement reactions. Some are not. Mark a check (✓) in the correct box next to each equation.

	Equation	Double replacement reaction	Not a double replacement reaction
1.	$Mg(OH_2) + 2HCl \rightarrow MgCl_2 + 2HOH$		
2.	$C_6H_{10}O_5 + H_2O \rightarrow C_6H_{12}O_6$		
3.	$Na_2SO_4 + BaCl_2 \rightarrow 2NaCl + BaSO_4$		
4.	$3Mg + N_2 \rightarrow Mg_3N_2$		
5.	$H_2SO_4 + BaCl_2 \rightarrow 2HCl + BaSO_4$		
6.	$ZnCO_3 \rightarrow ZnO + CO_2$		
7.	$CuSO_4 + H_2S \rightarrow H_2SO_4 + CuS$		
8.	$NH_4NO_3 \rightarrow 2H_2O + N_2O$		

IDENTIFYING CHEMICAL REACTIONS

Ten chemical equations are listed below. Identify each kind of reaction: synthesis, decomposition, single replacement, or double replacement.

	Equation	Kind of reaction
1.	$N_2 + 3H_2 \rightarrow 2NH_3$	
2.	$2Br_2 + 2H_2O \rightarrow 4HBr + O_2$	
3.	$Mg + 2HCl \rightarrow MgCl_2 + H_2$	
4.	$2KBr + H_2SO_4 \rightarrow K_2SO_4 + 2HBr$	
5.	$H_2SO_3 \rightarrow H_2O + SO_2$	
6.	$Na_2S + 2HCl \rightarrow 2NaCl + H_2S$	
7.	$2Na + I_2 \rightarrow 2NaI$	
8.	$NaCl + AgNO_3 \rightarrow NaNO_3 + AgCl$	
9.	$H_2 + Cl_2 \rightarrow 2HCl$	
10.	$H_2CO_3 \rightarrow H_2O + CO_2$	

What are oxidation and reduction?

oxidation [ahk-suh-DAY-shun]: linkup of oxygen with another substance; a loss of electrons

reduction [ri-DUK-shun]: separation of oxygen from a substance; a gain of electrons

LESSON 17 | What are oxidation and reduction?

Oxidation and reduction are opposite kinds of chemical reactions.

Oxidation [ahk-suh-DAY-shun] takes place when oxygen combines with another substance.

For example, when a flashbulb goes off, oxygen combines with aluminum.

The aluminum becomes oxidized. Aluminum oxide (Al_2O_3) forms.

$$4Al \quad + \quad 3O_2 \quad \longrightarrow \quad 2Al_2O_3$$
$$\text{Aluminum} \qquad \text{Oxygen} \qquad\qquad \text{Aluminum oxide}$$

Reduction [ri-DUK-shun] takes place when oxygen separates from a compound.

For example, electrolysis decomposes molten aluminum oxide (Al_2O_3). The oxygen separates from the aluminum. We say the aluminum oxide is reduced.

$$2Al_2O_3 \quad \longrightarrow \quad 4Al \quad + \quad 3O_2$$
$$\text{Aluminum oxide} \qquad\qquad \text{Aluminum} \qquad \text{Oxygen}$$

Here is another reduction equation. Notice what happens to the oxygen.

$$2Fe_2O_3 \quad + \quad 3C \longrightarrow 3CO_2 \quad + \quad 4Fe$$
$$\text{Iron oxide} \qquad \text{Carbon} \qquad \text{Carbon dioxide} \qquad \text{Iron}$$

The oxygen has separated from the iron. But the oxygen is not free oxygen. It is now part of the compound carbon dioxide. It makes no difference whether a separated oxygen becomes free oxygen or part of a new compound. As long as oxygen is separated from a compound, the reaction is reduction.

SLOW AND RAPID OXIDATION

Figure A   *Rusting is an example of slow oxidation.*

Figure B   *Fire is an example of rapid oxidation.*

UNDERSTANDING OXIDATION AND REDUCTION

Look at Figures C and D. Study the equations. Then answer the questions or fill in the blanks.

The burning of carbon

This equation describes what happens when carbon burns:

$$C + O_2 \longrightarrow CO_2$$

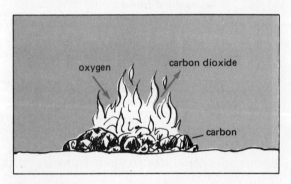

Figure C

1. Name the elements that react together when carbon burns.

   _____   _____

2. **a)** When carbon burns, oxygen _____ the carbon.
   <u>combines with, separates from</u>

   b) What product forms? _____

3. In oxidation, oxygen _____ another substance.
   <u>combines with, separates from</u>

4. In reduction, oxygen _____ a compound.
   <u>combines with, separates from</u>

5. When carbon burns, the carbon is _____ .
   <u>oxidized, reduced</u>

The electrolysis of water

The equation for the electrolysis of water is:

$$2H_2O \longrightarrow 2H_2 + O_2$$

6. Name the elements that make up water.

_____   _____

7. Electrolysis _____ water.

forms, decomposes

8. When water decomposes, oxygen

_____ hydrogen.

combines with, separates from

9. The separation of oxygen from a com
pound is called _____ .

oxidation, reduction

10. In the electrolysis of water, the hydrogen

is _____ .

oxidized, reduced

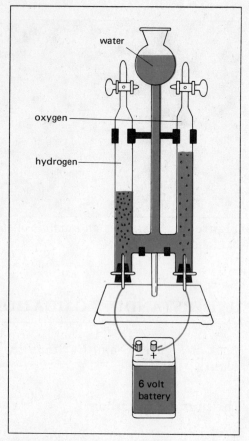

Figure D

ANOTHER VIEW OF OXIDATION AND REDUCTION

Oxidation combines oxygen with another substance.

Reduction separates oxygen from a compound.

This is true. But to a chemist, oxidation and reduction mean even more. A chemist thinks of oxidation and reduction in terms of <u>electrons lost</u> or <u>electrons gained</u>.

To a chemist,

* Oxidation means a loss of electrons.

* Reduction means a gain of electrons.

The reaction may or may not involve oxygen. This means that oxidation and reduction can happen without oxygen. All that is needed is a loss of electrons by one atom and the gain of electrons by some other atom.

Oxidation and reduction always happen together. It is easy to understand why...When one atom loses electrons, some other atom gains them.

Let us look at the burning of carbon and the electrolysis of water again. This time, look in terms of electrons gained and electrons lost.

THE BURNING OF CARBON

Look at Figure E. Answer the questions or fill in the blanks.

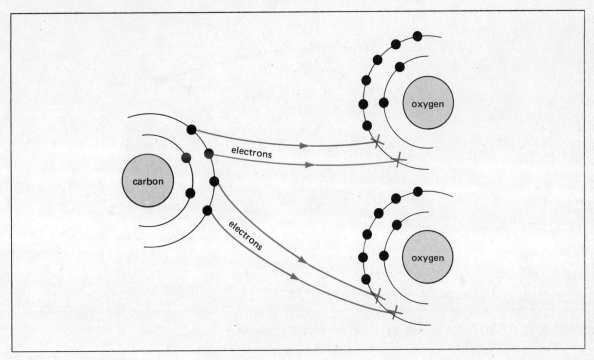

Figure E *What happens when carbon burns.*

1. When carbon burns, the carbon _____ electrons and the oxygen
   <u>lends, borrows</u>

   _____ electrons.
   <u>lends, borrows</u>

2. When carbon burns, the carbon _____ electrons and oxygen
   <u>gains, loses</u>

   _____ electrons.
   <u>gains, loses</u>

3. Oxidation is the _____ of electrons.
   <u>gain, loss</u>

4. Reduction is the _____ of electrons.
   <u>gain, loss</u>

5. When carbon burns, the carbon is _____ and the oxygen is
   <u>oxidized, reduced</u>

   _____ .
   <u>oxidized, reduced</u>

6. Oxidation and reduction happen together because electrons _____ by

   one atom are _____ by some other atom.

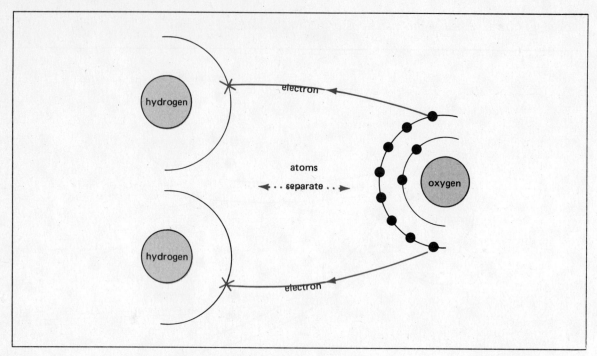

Figure F *What happens during the electrolysis of water.*

7. Electrolysis _____ water.
   forms, decomposes

8. When water decomposes, electrons move from the _____ to the
   hydrogen, oxygen

   _____ .
   hydrogen, oxygen

9. The hydrogen _____ electrons and the oxygen _____
   gains, loses   gains, loses

   electrons.

10. Oxidation is the _____ of electrons.
    gain, loss

11. Reduction is the _____ of electrons.
    gain, loss

12. During the electrolysis of water, the hydrogen is _____ and the
    oxidized, reduced

    oxygen is _____ .
    oxidized, reduced

13. Why do oxidation and reduction always happen together? _____

    _____

OXIDATION OR REDUCTION

Each equation listed below is either an oxidation or a reduction reaction. Which one is it? Put a check (✓) in the correct box next to each equation.

	Equation	Oxidation	Reduction
1.	$2Ba + O_2 \rightarrow 2BaO$		
2.	$2HgO \rightarrow 2Hg + O_2$		
3.	$ZnO + C \rightarrow Zn + CO$		
4.	$4Na + O_2 \rightarrow 2Na_2O$		
5.	$CuO + H_2 \rightarrow Cu + H_2O$		
6.	$N_2 + O_2 \rightarrow 2NO$		
7.	$4Ag + O_2 \rightarrow 2Ag_2O$		
8.	$SnO_2 + 2C \rightarrow Sn + 2CO$		
9.	$C + O_2 \rightarrow CO_2$		
10.	$Fe_2O_3 + 3CO \rightarrow 2Fe + 3CO_2$		

REACHING OUT

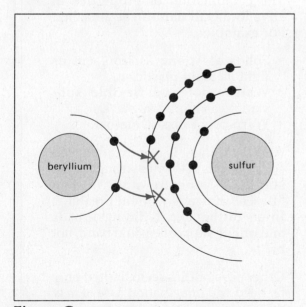

Figure G

Beryllium links up with sulfur to form beryllium sulfide.

$$Be + S \longrightarrow BeS$$

No oxygen is involved in this reaction. Yet it is an oxidation-reduction reaction.

Why is this an oxidation-reduction reac-

tion? _____

_____

_____

SCIENCE*EXTRA*

Futuristic Materials — Today!

The house stands in Pittsfield, Massachusetts. It is very attractive. Yet this house built by General Electric Corporation is one of a kind. It is an experimental home built almost entirely from a new class of souped-up products called <u>advanced materials</u>.

Advanced materials are really futuristic changes of present-day plastics, ceramics, glass, and metals. Additional ingredients are added in a specific way to a basic material. This improves the basic material's performance, or gives it new properties, or both.

For example:

- The addition of thin carbon fibers results in a plastic ten times stronger and also lighter in weight than standard plastic.
- An alloy of copper, aluminum, and zinc creates a metal with a memory. No matter how much it is bent or twisted, it returns to its original shape. It remembers!

Let's look at the GE home again. Its sides are covered not with regular wood, aluminum, vinyl, or even brick. It is clad with a superstrong and highly insulating advanced plastic. Even the roof shingles, floors, doorframes, plumbing pipes and fixtures, and windows are made of souped-up materials.

The combination of properties in advanced materials can be amazing. For example:

- Solids as strong as iron, but as light as foam plastic.
- Waterproof and flexible substances as strong as steel.
- Warp-proof plastic lumber.

And then, there is a truly advanced <u>concrete</u>. It is 100 times stronger than standard concrete and it also "flexes." It bends without breaking. In an earthquake, buildings, roads and bridge supports would bend, not break.

Other possibilities seem limited only by need and imagination. Use of new materials will help us conserve our natural resources such as metals and wood.

What is an ore?

mineral: a solid substance found in the earth's crust
ore: a mineral that contains a useful amount of metal
metallurgy: the science of separating metals from the ores in which they are found
metallurgist: a scientist who studies metals

LESSON 18 | What is an ore?

Towering skyscrapers, graceful bridges that support millions of kilograms, huge ocean liners, trucks, trains, food cans, even ballpoint pens... These are part of our modern world. They all have one thing in common. They could not be possible without metal.

Modern civilization depends upon metals. Yet, we take them for granted. Did you ever wonder where metals come from?

Most metals are found in the earth's crust. (We live on the earth's crust.) A few metals, like gold and silver, are found as native or free **minerals**. That is, they are not part of any compound. Most metals, however, are combined chemically with other elements. They are part of mineral compounds.

Mineral compounds may be decomposed. This frees the metals so we can use them.

A mineral that can supply a useful metal at reasonable cost is called an **ore**.

There are three main groups of ores: oxides, sulfides, and carbonates.

OXIDES Oxides are compounds of oxygen. Hematite is an example of an oxide ore. Hematite, or iron oxide (Fe_2O_3), is the chief iron ore.

SULFIDES Sulfides are compounds of sulfur. Galena is an example of a sulfur ore. Galena, or lead sulfide (PbS), is the chief lead ore.

CARBONATES Carbonates are compounds containing the polyatomic ion CO_3^{-2}. Smithsonite is an example of a carbonate ore. Smithsonite, or zinc carbonate ($ZnCO_3$), is an important zinc ore.

There are several ways to separate ores. The method used depends upon the ore. You will learn how metals are separated from their ores in the next lesson.

The science of separating metals from ores is called **metallurgy** [MET-uh-lur-jee]. A scientist who studies metals is called a **metallurgist**.

UNDERSTANDING ORES

Figure A

Most ores look like ordinary rocks. You would not guess that they contain shiny metal.

The earth's crust is made up of many minerals.

People have discovered more than 2000 different minerals. Many of these contain metals. But because the metal elements are linked with other elements in the minerals, the metals do not show all of their properties.

1. Most minerals are _____ .
   <u>elements, compounds</u>

2. In order to free the metal from the other elements, a mineral must be

   _____ .
   <u>synthesized, decomposed</u>

Figure B

Figure C

Some ores are mined deep in the ground as in Figure B. However, most ores are mined on the surface. This is called <u>open-pit</u> mining. Figure C shows a huge open pit mine.

3. What is the definition of an ore? _____

   _____

4. Many minerals contain metal.

   a) Is every mineral that contains a metal an ore? _____

   b) Why or why not? _____

   _____

IDENTIFYING METALS FROM THEIR ORES

The chart below lists some important ores and their formulas.

Which metal do we get from each ore? Look at the formulas. See which metals are shown by their symbols. Write your answers in the column next to the formulas. Then decide if the ore is an oxide, sulfide, or carbonate. Write your answers in the last column.

	Ore	Formula	Metal	Oxide, Sulfide, or Carbonate?
1.	hematite	Fe_2O_3		
2.	galena	PbS		
3.	cinnabar	HgS		
4.	siderite	$FeCO_3$		
5.	bauxite	Al_2O_3		
6.	cassiterite	SnO_2		
7.	magnesite	$MgCO_3$		
8.	smithsonite	$ZnCO_3$		
9.	uraninite	UO_2		
10.	litharge	PbO		
11.	magnetite	Fe_3O_4		
12.	sphalerite	ZnS		
13.	cuprite	Cu_2O		
14.	limonite	Fe_2O_3		
15.	zincite	ZnO		
16.	pyrite	FeS_2		

In some of these ores, the metals give the mineral a metallic luster. Examples are the iron ores hematite, magnetite, and pyrite. Other ores, such as bauxite and cassiterite, are dull, even though they contain the metals aluminum and tin.

ELEMENTS OF THE EARTH'S CRUST

The pie graph in Figure D shows the percentage of the most common elements that make up the earth's crust.

Study the graph. Then answer the questions.

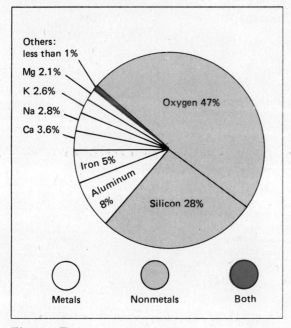

Figure D

1. Most of the earth's crust is made up of _____ .

   metals, nonmetals

2. The most common element of the earth's crust is _____ .

3. The second most common element of the earth's crust is _____ .

4. a) Together, oxygen and silicon make up _____ percent of the earth's crust.

   b) Write the percent as a fraction.

   _____

5. a) The most common metal of the earth's crust is _____ .

   b) What percentage of the crust is it? _____

6. a) The second most common metal of the earth's crust is _____ .

   b) What percentage of the crust is it? _____

7. The six metals named in the graph make up about what percent of the earth's crust? _____

MATCHING

Match each term in Column A with its description in Column B. Write the correct letter in the space provided.

Column A	Column B
_____ 1. crust	a) iron ore
_____ 2. carbonate	b) lead ore
_____ 3. hematite	c) the part of the earth on which we live
_____ 4. smithsonite	d) zinc ore
_____ 5. galena	e) CO_3

FILL IN THE BLANK

Complete each statement using a term or terms from the list below. Write your answers in the spaces provided.

crust   sulfides   ore
metallurgist   gold   silver
decomposed   carbonates   oxides
minerals   more   metallurgy

1. Most metals are found in the earth's _____ .

2. Metals found not combined with other elements are called native elements or native

   _____ .

3. Examples of native minerals are _____ and _____ .

4. Most minerals are made up of _____ than one element.

5. To separate a metal from its mineral, the mineral must be _____ .

6. A mineral that can supply a useful metal at reasonable cost is called an

   _____ .

7. Most ores are compounds called _____ , _____ , or

   _____ .

8. The study of taking metals from ores and making them useful is called

   _____ .

9. A scientist who studies metals and ores is called a _____ .

REACHING OUT

1. What does recycle mean? _____

   _____

2. Why should metals be recycled?

   _____

   _____

   _____

Figure E

How can we free a metal from its ore?

roasting: heating an ore in the open air
reducing agent: a material that takes the oxygen out of an ore
coke: a form of carbon that reacts with oxide ores

LESSON 19 | How can we free a metal from its ore?

Can we use copper ore right out of the ground to make a copper wire? Of course not. A metal must be separated from its ore before it can be used. The method used to separate an ore depends on its chemistry.

First let's look at oxide ores. The metal of an oxide ore is combined with oxygen. To free the metal we must reduce the ore. Reduction removes the oxygen and frees the metal. Carbon may be used to reduce an oxide ore. We call the carbon a **reducing agent**. The carbon is heated with the ore.

Let's look at how carbon can reduce copper oxide ore when we heat them together.

OXIDE ORE (Copper Oxide)

REDUCTION $2CuO$ + C → $2Cu$ + CO_2
             Copper oxide   Carbon   Copper   Carbon dioxide

In this reaction the carbon and oxygen link up to form carbon dioxide. This sets the copper free.

Metals cannot be freed so easily from sulfide and carbonate ores. It takes two steps: 1. The ores are heated in the open air. This is called **roasting**. Roasting turns the sulfide or carbonate ore into an oxide. 2. Then the oxide can be reduced. The metal is set free. Look at the examples below.

SULFIDE ORE (Copper sulfide)

Step 1 $2CuS$ + $3O_2$ → $2CuO$ + $2SO_2$
ROASTING   Copper sulfide   Oxygen   Copper oxide   Sulfur dioxide

Step 2 $2CuO$ + C → $2Cu$ + CO_2
REDUCTION   Copper oxide   Carbon   Copper   Carbon dioxide

CARBONATE ORE (Zinc carbonate)

Step 1 $ZnCO_3$ → ZnO + CO_2
ROASTING   Zinc carbonate   Zinc oxide   Carbon dioxide

Step 2 $2ZnO$ + C → $2Zn$ + CO_2
REDUCTION   Zinc oxide   Carbon   Zinc   Carbon dioxide

Look at Figures A and B and read the explanations with each. Then answer the questions.

Freeing copper from copper oxide

Figure A shows how copper oxide can be reduced in a laboratory.

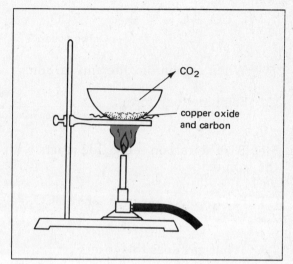

Figure A

1. What ore is being reduced?

   _____

2. What is the reducing agent?

   _____

3. What gas is released?

   _____

4. What metal is freed?

   _____

Freeing iron from iron oxide

Iron oxide ores are usually reduced in huge blast furnaces at high temperatures.

Figure B shows what happens when the iron ore hematite (Fe_2O_3) is reduced.

Follow the decomposition of hematite step by step.

Step 1 **Coke** (a form of carbon) and hematite are put into the furnace. The coke burns.

$$C + O_2 \rightarrow CO_2$$

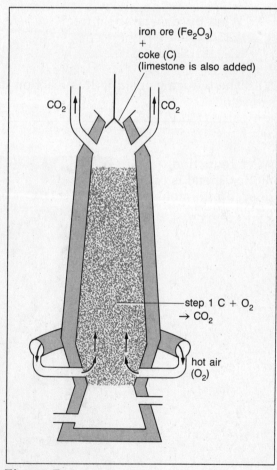

Figure B

5. When coke (carbon) burns, it combines with _____ .
   <u>oxygen, carbon dioxide</u>

6. When carbon links up with oxygen it forms _____ .
   <u>carbon dioxide, hematite</u>

119

Step 2   Some of the carbon dioxide and the carbon react together.

$$CO_2 + C \rightarrow 2CO$$
Carbon monoxide

7. When carbon dioxide and carbon combine they form _____.
   oxygen, carbon monoxide

Step 3   The carbon monoxide reacts with the iron oxide.

$$Fe_2O_3 + 3CO \rightarrow 2Fe + 3CO_2$$

8. What gas does this form?

   _____

9. What pure metal is set free?

   _____

10. The reducing agent in this reaction is

   _____ .
   carbon, carbon dioxide, carbon monoxide

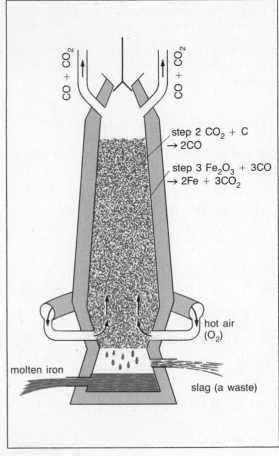

Figure C

After reduction, molten metal is often poured into molds called pigs.

Figure D

METALS FROM SULFIDE ORES

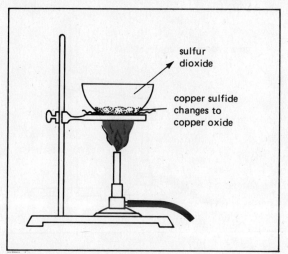

Figure E

Purpose To free the copper from sulfide (CuS)

What You Need (Materials)

10 grams of copper sulfide
powdered charcoal (carbon)
crucible
ring stand
wire gauze
Bunsen burner
Pyrex test tube
hand clamp
long iron wire (or nail)

What To Do (Procedure)

Step 1

1. Place the copper sulfide into the crucible.

2. Heat it with a high flame for about 15 minutes.

3. Stir from time to time with the iron wire.

The heat causes a chemical reaction. This is the equation:

$$2CuS + 3O_2 \rightarrow 2CuO + 2SO_2$$

Copper sulfide — Oxygen — Copper oxide — Sulfur dioxide

Answer the questions.

4. The copper sulfide reacts with _____ from the air.

5. The oxygen combines with two elements:_____ and _____.

6. The copper sulfide changes to _____.

7. **a)** We smell something like rotten eggs. What gas causes this odor? _____

   b) What happens to this gas?_____

8. What stays behind in the dish? _____

9. Is the copper free? _____

10. What is this first step called? _____

11. One more step is needed to free the copper. What is it called? _____

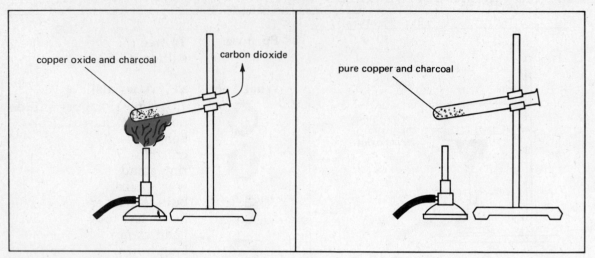

Figure F

Step 2

12. Wait for the crucible to cool.

13. Add some of the powdered charcoal to the copper oxide. Mix them.

14. Place the mixture into the Pyrex test tube. Heat with a high flame.

Another chemical reaction takes place. This is the equation:

$$2CuO \quad + \quad C \quad \rightarrow \quad 2Cu \quad + \quad CO_2$$

Copper oxide   Carbon   Copper   Carbon dioxide

15. The carbon removes the oxygen from the copper oxide. This is called

    _____ .
      oxidation, reduction

16. With what does the carbon combine? _____

17. What does the linkup of the carbon and oxygen form? _____

18. What is left behind? _____

19. The first step in freeing a metal from sulfide ore is called roasting. What is this

    second step called? _____

METALS FROM CARBONATE ORES

Purpose   To free lead from lead carbonate ($PbCO_3$)

What You Need (Materials)

Use the same equipment you used in the previous experiment with one exception.
Instead of 10 grams of copper sulfide, use 10 grams of lead carbonate.

What To Do (Procedure)

Step 1

1. Place the lead carbonate into the crucible. Heat it with a high flame for about 15 minutes.

2. Stir from time to time with the wire.

   The heat causes a chemical reaction. This is the equation:

   $$PbCO_3 \rightarrow PbO + CO_2$$

   Lead carbonate   Lead oxide   Carbon dioxide

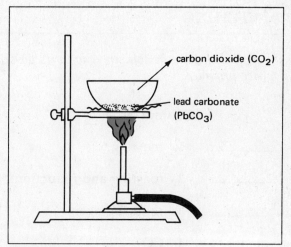

Figure G

3. The lead carbonate _____ .

   oxidizes, reduces, decomposes

4. Heat decomposes lead carbonate to _____and _____

5. What happens to the carbon dioxide? _____

6. What happens to the lead oxide? _____

7. This first step in freeing metal from a carbonate is called _____ .

Step 2

8. Wait for the crucible to cool.

9. Add some of the powdered charcoal to the lead oxide. Mix.

10. Place the mixture into the test tube. Heat it with a high flame.

    Another chemical reaction takes place. This is the equation:

    $$2PbO + C \rightarrow CO_2 + 2Pb$$

    Lead Oxide Carbon   Carbon dioxide   Lead

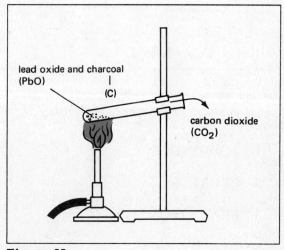

Figure H

11. The carbon removes the oxygen from the lead oxide. What is this process called?

    _____

12. With what does the carbon combine? _____

13. The linkup of carbon and oxygen forms _____ .

14. What is left behind? _____

15. Two steps are needed to free a metal from a carbonate ore. Name them in order.

    _____   _____

123

MATCHING

Match each term in column A with its description in Column B. Write the correct letter in the space provided.

Column A

_____ 1. roasting

_____ 2. roasting and reduction

_____ 3. reducing agent

_____ 4. CO

_____ 5. CO_2

Column B

a) steps in separating sulfide and carbonate ores

b) removes oxygen from a compound

c) forms when carbon and CO_2 combine

d) heating an ore in the open air

e) carbon dioxide

WORD SCRAMBLE

Below are several scrambled words you have used in this Lesson. Unscramble the words and write your answers in the spaces provided.

1. TORIDNUCE _____

2. CREANITO _____

3. BRACATEON _____

4. DEXIO _____

5. SPEEDCOOMS _____

6. FEDILUS _____

What is an alloy?

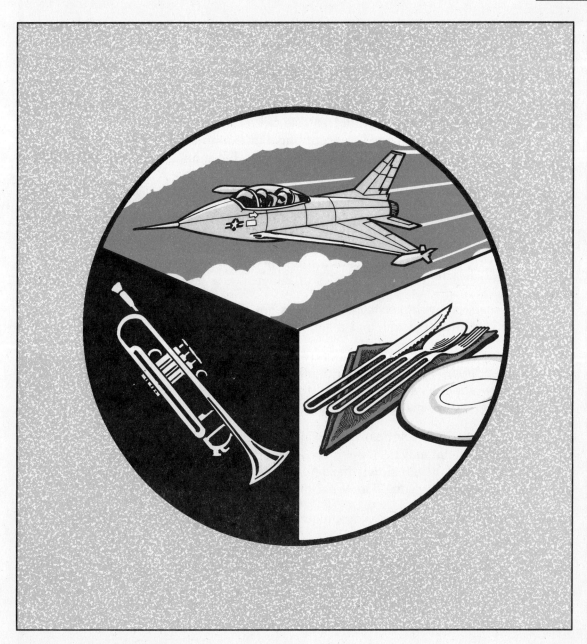

alloy: a blend of metals

LESSON 20 | What is an alloy?

All metals share certain properties. But no two metals have exactly the same properties. For example, some are lighter or stronger than others. Some shine more. Some melt more easily or conduct electricity better than others.

Often, a manufacturer wants to use a certain metal. It has all the properties that are needed—except one. For example, the metal may be strong enough, but it rusts easily. What can be done?

METALLURGISTS TO THE RESCUE!

Metallurgists have learned to custom-make metals. They mix and blend two or more metals. This mixing changes certain properties.

A mixture of metals that acts as a single metal is called an **alloy**. Stainless steel and Duralumin are examples of alloys.

Iron rusts easily. But stainless steel does not. Stainless steel is an alloy of iron, chromium, nickel, and a small amount of carbon.

Aluminum is light. But it is not strong. Duralumin is an alloy of aluminum, copper, magnesium, and manganese. Duralumin is light and strong—about as strong as steel. It is used in airplanes. Some automobile engines are made of this tough alloy.

Your dentist fills cavities with an alloy of silver and some other metal. The other metal may be copper, tin, zinc, or mercury. The alloy starts out like a sticky putty. It slowly hardens after it is mixed. Why do you think your dentist tells you, "Don't eat on that side for at least one hour?"

There are thousands of alloys. New alloys are being discovered all the time.

Most metal products we use are not pure metals. They are alloys.

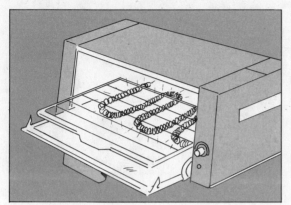

Figure A

Nichrome [NIE-krome] is an alloy of nickel, chromium, iron, and manganese. Nichrome wire has a high electrical resistance. It gives off a great deal of heat when electricity moves through it. The heating elements of electric irons and toasters are made of nichrome.

Any steel is an alloy of iron and other metals. It is very strong. If vanadium is added to steel, the steel becomes even stronger. Automobile frames, gears, springs, and axles are made of vanadium steel.

Figure B

Solder [SOD-er] is an alloy. There are many kinds of solder. One common solder is a blend of tin and lead. Solder melts easily and can join two pieces of metal.

Figure C

Figure D

Chromium steel has great hardness. It is used in making bank vaults, special tools, and armor plate.

Figure E

Costume jewelry is rarely pure gold or pure silver. It is made of an alloy. A small amount of cheap metal is added to the gold or silver. This addition serves two purposes: it lessens the cost, and it makes the gold or silver harder.

Figure F

The earliest alloy was bronze. Bronze is a blend of copper and tin. It was discovered (probably by accident) about 5,000 years ago.

Bronze is very hard and durable. It was widely used for knives, spearheads, battle axes, helmets, shields, and swords. Early cups and vases were also made of bronze.

Today, bronze is used for things like statues, coins, and lamps. Our copper penny is really a bronze alloy.

MAKING WOOD'S METAL

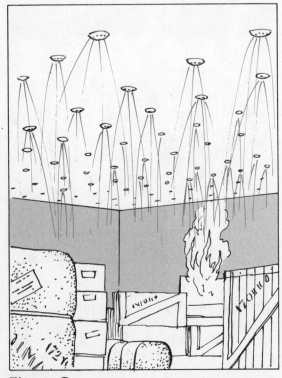

Figure G

Wood's metal is an alloy of bismuth, cadmium, tin, and lead. It melts at a low temperature—70° C (158° F). This is lower than the boiling point of water. Wood's metal is used as plugs in automatic fire sprinklers. Heat from a fire quickly melts this metal, and the water sprinkles out. Why not make your own alloy?

What You Need (Materials)

crucible
tripod
Bunsen burner
iron wire (or nail)
metal tongs
heat-resistant pad
Pyrex beaker
bismuth—20 grams
lead—10 grams
tin—5 grams
cadmium—5 grams

How To Do the Experiment (Procedure)

Figure H

iron

mixture of bismuth, lead, tin, & cadmium

CAD   BISM   LEAD   TIN

"sprinkles" of bismuth, lead, tin & cadmium

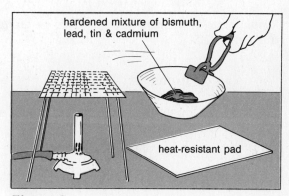

Figure I

hardened mixture of bismuth, lead, tin & cadmium

heat-resistant pad

1. Place the metals into the crucible. Leave out just a few "sprinkles" of each metal.

2. Heat the crucible. Stir the metals with the iron wire until the mixture is melted.

3. Remove the crucible with the tongs. Place it on the heat-resistant pad. Let the mixture cool and harden.

Figure J

"sprinklings" of bismuth, lead, tin & cadmium

no melting

Figure K

4. Boil some water in the beaker.

5. One at a time, sprinkle the separate metals into the boiling water. Notice what happens.

6. Pry the hardened metal from the crucible. Drop it carefully into the boiling water. (DON'T SPLASH!)

What You Saw (Observations)

1. The separate metals _____ melt when you sprinkled them in boiling

did, did not

   water. But the hardened mixture _____ melt.

did, did not

2. The hardened mixture _____ an alloy.

is, is not

3. What is its name? _____

Something To Think About (Conclusions)

1. Wood's metal melts at a _____ temperature than the metals that
   make it up.   higher, lower

FILL IN THE BLANK

Complete each statement using a term or terms from the list below. Write your answers in the spaces provided.

strong	alloy	metals
alloys	same	special
custom-made	melted together	metallurgists
lightness		

1. All metals have certain properties that are the _____ .

2. Every metal has certain _____ properties.

3. A special property of aluminum is its _____ .

4. Aluminum is not very _____ .

5. Aluminum can be made stronger when it is mixed with certain other

   _____ .

6. A mixture of metals that acts as a single metal is called an _____ .

7. An alloy can be called a _____ metal.

8. The metals of most alloys are _____ .

9. "Recipes" for alloys are figured out by _____ .

10. Most metal products we use are _____ .

MATCHING

Match each term in Column A with its description in Column B. Write the correct letter in the space provided.

Column A		Column B
_____	1. alloy	a) non-rusting iron alloy
_____	2. stainless steel	b) rusts
_____	3. Duralumin	c) first alloy
_____	4. bronze	d) any blend of metals
_____	5. iron	e) light and strong

How do we electroplate metals?

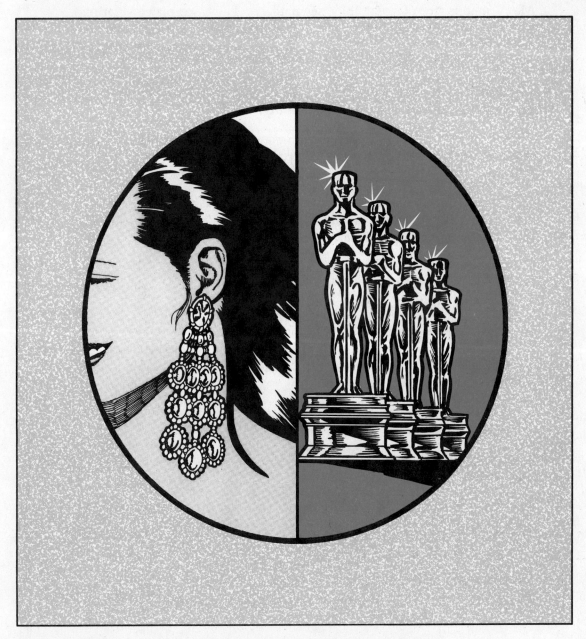

electroplating: putting a coating on a metal by using electricity

LESSON 21 | How do we electroplate metals?

Many metals aren't what they seem to be. They are plated. Plating places a thin layer of one metal upon another metal. Some metals are plated by hot-dipping. Most metals, however, are plated by **electroplating.**

Electroplating protects metals. It also makes metals look better. Most electroplated metals are bright and shiny.

The metal trim on some furniture, for example, is made of steel. Steel is not very shiny. When steel is electroplated with chromium, it gets a bright shine. Chromium also protects steel from corrosion.

Electroplating is often used only for appearance. Gold and silver are attractive, but expensive, metals. Many pieces of "gold" and "silver" jewelry are really mostly cheap metal. They are just electroplated with gold or silver.

Electroplating is easy to do. It is explained below. Check with Figure A, on the facing page, as you read.

1. Electroplating is done in a liquid <u>salt solution</u>. There are many kinds of salts. The salt you use must contain the metal you want to deposit. For example, if you want to plate a metal with silver, you use a salt like silver nitrate ($AgNO_3$).

2. Connect the metal you want to deposit (such as silver) to the anode. The anode is the positive (+) electric pole.

3. Connect the metal you want to coat to the cathode. The cathode is the negative (—) electric pole.

4. Pass a weak direct electrical current through the solution.

The metal you wanted to coat becomes plated with the metal of the salt solution. In our example that metal is silver.

The thickness of the plate depends upon how long the electricity flows. The longer it flows, the thicker the plate becomes. But even a "thick" plate is very thin.

UNDERSTANDING ELECTROPLATING

Look at Figures A and B. Then answer the questions or fill in the blanks.

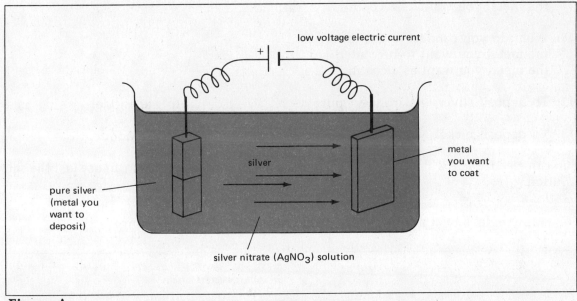

Figure A

1. Electroplating is done _____ .

in air, in a liquid solution

2. The solution used in electroplating contains a dissolved _____ .

salt, gas

3. The salt of an electroplating solution must contain the metal _____

_____ .

you are coating, you want to deposit

4. Silver nitrate solution can deposit the metal _____ .

5. Copper sulfate can deposit the metal _____ .

6. Gold cyanide can deposit the metal _____ .

7. Electroplating uses _____ current.

strong direct, weak direct, weak alternating

A source of electricity has two poles: <u>positive</u> and <u>negative</u>.

8. The positive pole is called the _____ .

anode, cathode

9. The negative pole is called the _____ .

anode, cathode

In the next two questions, place a check mark next to the answer you choose.

10. In electroplating, what do connect to the anode?
    the metal you want to be coated. _____
    the metal you want as a coating. _____

11. What do you connect to the cathode?
    the metal you want to be coated. _____
    the metal you want as a coating. _____

12. To deposit silver, you connect pure _____ to the anode.

13. To deposit nickel, you connect pure _____ to the anode.

You can electroplate without a pure metal connected to the anode. You can use just the salt solution.

For example, let's look at our silver-plating setup with the one change.

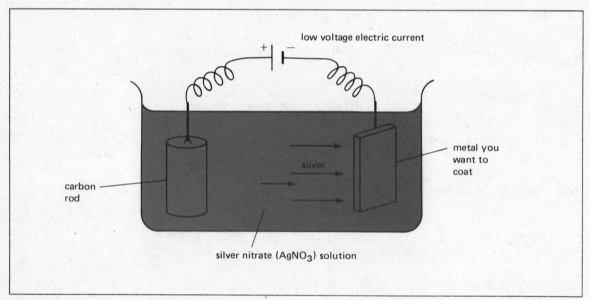

Figure B

A plain carbon rod has taken the place of the silver. The silver plate comes from the silver nitrate solution only.

14. Plating this way can produce only a thin coat or can coat only a few pieces. Why?

_____

_____

_____

IDENTIFYING PARTS IN ELECTROPLATING

Four electroplating setups are shown in Figures C through F. One part of each setup is labeled. Two parts are not labeled. Identify the parts that are not labeled. Write your answers on the lines under each diagram. (Hint: Check terminals carefully!) Choose from the following :

gold cyanide solution
zinc coat
pure nickel
nickel coat

tin coat
pure gold
zinc chloride solution
pure tin

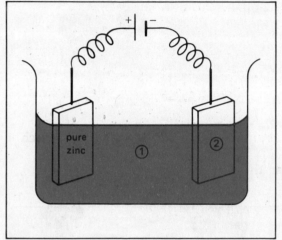

Figure C

1. _____

2. _____

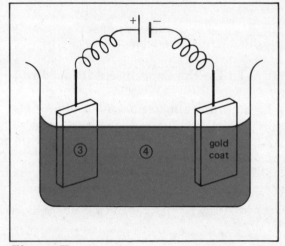

Figure D

3. _____

4. _____

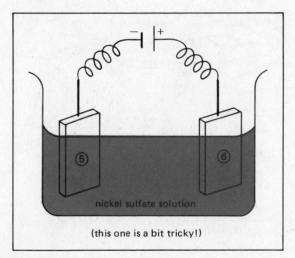

Figure E

5. _____

6. _____

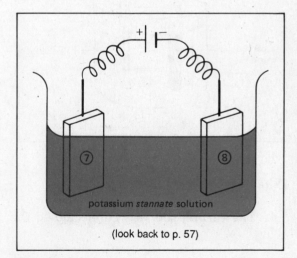

Figure F

7. _____

8. _____

EXPERIMENTING WITH ELECTROPLATING

What You Need To Know (Background Information)

- The color of carbon is black.
- The color of iron is silver-gray.
- The color of copper is reddish-orange.

What You Need (Materials)

glass beaker
copper sulfate solution
two metal clips
one carbon rod
one clean iron nail

two dry cells
wire
switch
file

How To Do the Experiment (Procedure)

1. Set up the materials as in Figure G.

2. Pass electricity through the solution for about 5 minutes. Then open the switch.

3. Remove the carbon rod and nail. Examine them.

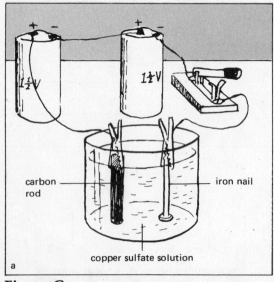

Figure G

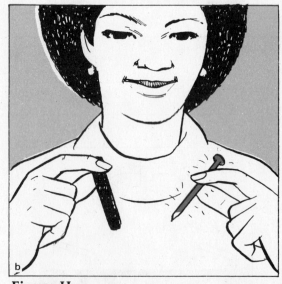

Figure H

What You Saw (Observations)

4. The carbon rod was connected to the _____ .

anode, cathode

5. The iron nail was connected to the _____ .

anode, cathode

6. Which became plated, the carbon or the iron? _____

7. How do you know? _____

8. What color is the plate? _____

9. What metal is the plate? _____

10. Where did the plate metal come from? _____

NOW gently file the head of the nail.

11. The plating _____ file off easily.
           did, did not

12. This shows that the plating is _____ .
                                        thick, thin

Something To Think About (Conclusions)

1. If you pass electricity through the solution longer, the plate becomes

_____ .
   thicker, thinner

2. If you wish to coat many pieces, what must you connect to the anode?

_____

FILL IN THE BLANK

Complete each statement using a term or terms from the list below. Write your answers in the spaces provided.

negative	look better	hot-dipping
weak	replaces	positive
plate	thin	electroplating
protects	salt solution	

1. Plating places a _____ layer of one metal upon another metal.

2. Some plating, like tinning and galvanizing, is done by _____ .

3. Plating that uses electricity is called _____ .

4. Electroplating is done with _____ direct electrical current.

5. Electroplating _____ metals. Electroplating also makes metals

_____ .

6. Electroplating is done in a _____ .

7. The salt you use in electroplating must contain the metal you wish as the _____ .

8. The metal you want to cover is connected to the _____ electrical pole.

9. The pure metal you want as the plating is connected to the _____ pole.

10. The pure metal _____ the metal from the solution that is used up.

In solution, a salt breaks up into ions. An ion, you remember, has a charge.

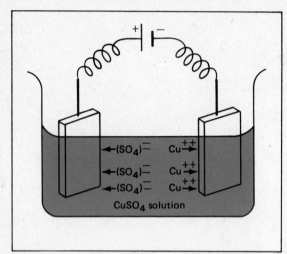

For example, in solution, copper sulfate ($CuSO_4$) breaks up into:

- positively charged copper ions (Cu^{+2}), and
- negatively charged sulfate ions (SO_4^{-2}).

The copper ions move towards the negative pole. The sulfate ions move towards the positive pole.

Figure I

a) Why do the ions move towards these poles? _____

_____

A plus or positive ion is an atom that has lost one or more of its electrons.

b) In copper sulfate, how many electrons has each copper ion lost? _____

c) Where do the copper ions pick up these electrons again? _____

_____

d) What does each copper ion become when it picks up the electrons it has lost?

_____

What is metal activity? | 22

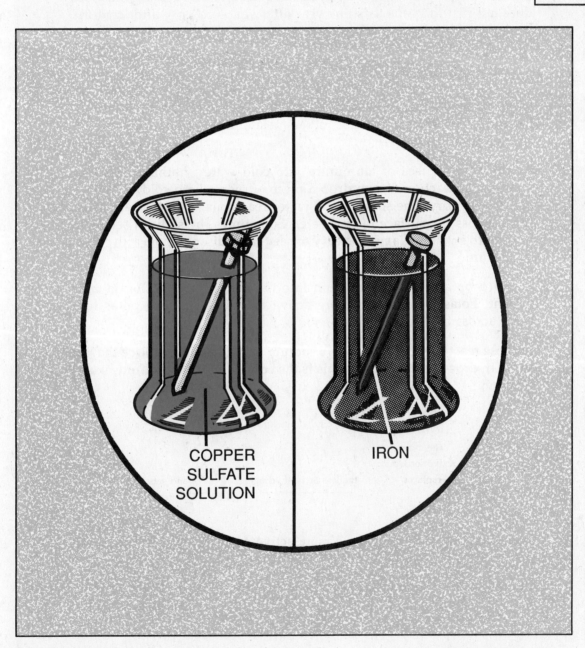

COPPER
SULFATE
SOLUTION

IRON

metal activity: the ease with which metals react with other elements to form positive metal ions

LESSON 22 | What is metal activity?

You have seen rusted iron. But you have never seen rusted gold. Gold does not rust. It keeps its shine year after year—century after century.

Iron forms compounds. So does gold. But iron forms compounds more easily than gold does. We say that iron is more active than gold. This means iron lends electrons more easily than gold.

Different metals have different activities. Some metals react with water, for example, more easily than other metals. Lets compare aluminum and sodium.

If you drop a piece of aluminum into cold water, nothing happens. There is no reaction. If you drop a piece of sodium into cold water, it's a different story! The sodium and water react immediately. The sodium races across the surface of the water. Sometimes the sodium seems to burn with a yellow flame. It's easy to see that sodium is <u>more active</u> than aluminum.

If you drop a piece of potassium into the water, the reaction is more violent. Potassium is even more active than sodium. The potassium races across the water even faster.

In these reactions, the more active sodium and potassium <u>replace</u> the less active hydrogen of the water. This is the equation for the sodium/water reaction.

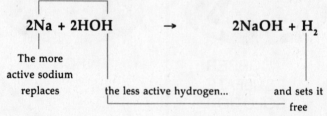

$$2Na + 2HOH \rightarrow 2NaOH + H_2$$

The more active sodium replaces   the less active hydrogen...   and sets it free

In any replacement reaction, a more active metal replaces a less active metal.

Chemists know how active each metal is. The table on the next page lists the metals in the order of their activity. This table of **metal activity** lets us predict many chemical reactions.

UNDERSTANDING METAL ACTIVITY

A table of **metal activity** is shown on the right. It lists the metals according to their activity. Study the table. Then answer the questions.

More Active		Less Active
Lithium	Li	
Potassium	K	
Barium	Ba	
Calcium	Ca	
Sodium	Na	
Magnesium	Mg	
Aluminum	Al	
Zinc	Zn	
Iron	Fe	
Tin	Sn	
Lead	Pb	
Hydrogen*	H	
Copper	Cu	
Mercury	Hg	
Silver	Ag	
Platinum	Pt	
Gold	Au	

1. Which is the most active metal?

   _____

2. Which is the least active metal?

   _____

3. Which is correct? (Circle the correct answer.)

   A less active metal can replace a more active metal

   A more active metal can replace a less active metal

4. Which is more active,

   sodium or iron? _____   gold or silver? _____

   tin or lead? _____   tin or aluminum? _____

5. Which is less active,

   sodium or calcium? _____   copper or mercury? _____

   zinc or tin? _____   hydrogen or platinum? _____

6. Name the metals that can replace calcium. _____

   _____

7. Name the metals that cannot replace mercury. _____

   _____

8. Which is the only metal that can replace potassium? _____

9. Can any metal replace lithium? _____

   Why or why not? _____

10. Can gold replace any metal? _____

    Why or why not? _____

    _____

*Hydrogen is included for reference.

TESTING METAL ACTIVITY BETWEEN COPPER AND IRON SULFATE

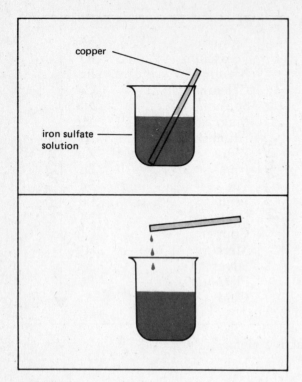

Figure A

What You Need (Materials)

strip of copper
iron sulfate solution
beaker

How To Do the Test (Procedure)

1. Place the copper strip into the iron sulfate solution.

2. Wait 3 to 4 minutes. Then remove the copper strip.

   Examine it carefully.

What You Saw (Observations)

3. Did the strip change color? _____

   Did the solution change color? _____

4. A chemical reaction _____ take place.
   _{did, did not}

5. The copper _____ become coated with iron.
   _{did, did not}

6. The copper _____ replace the iron of the iron sulfate.
   _{did, did not}

7. Which is less active, iron or copper? (Check the table.) _____

8. Which is more active, iron or copper? _____

9. Can a less active metal replace a more active metal? _____

10. Why didn't the copper replace the iron? _____

11. Can a chemical equation show what happened? _____

    Why or why not? _____

142

TESTING METAL ACTIVITY BETWEEN IRON AND COPPER SULFATE

What You Need (Materials)

beaker
iron nail
copper sulfate solution

What You Need To Know (Background Information)

Iron is silver-gray in color.
Copper sulfate is blue.
Iron sulfate is green.

How To Do the Experiment (Procedure)

1. Place the nail into the copper sulfate solution.

2. Wait 3 to 4 minutes. Then remove the nail. Examine the nail and the solution.

iron nail
copper sulfate solution

What You Learned (Observations)

3. Did the nail change color? _____ What color? _____

4. Did the solution change color? _____ What color? _____

5. A chemical reaction _____ take place.
   did, did not

The following equation shows what happened:

$$Fe \quad + \quad CuSO_4 \quad \rightarrow \quad Cu \quad + \quad FeSO_4$$

Iron   Copper sulfate   Copper   Iron sulfate

6. Which is correct? (Circle the correct answer.)

   The iron replaced the copper.

   The copper replaced the iron.

Something To Think About (Conclusions)

1. Which is more active, iron or copper? _____

2. Which is less active, iron or copper? _____

3. Why did the iron replace the copper? _____

4. Which metal did the reaction set free? _____

5. What happened to it? _____

6. Why did the solution turn green? _____

SCIENCE *EXTRA*

Electroplater

Many things that look like metal really aren't metal all the way through. Take most household water faucets, for example. They shine like metal. But that metal is <u>very</u> thin — only about 1/1,000 of an inch thick. The rest (and this may surprise you), is treated <u>plastic</u>. The shiny metal surface was electroplated on the plastic.

Electroplating is the process of putting a metal coat on another metal or some other conducting surface. The thickness of the coat depends upon the strength of the electric current and the length of plating time. Electroplating is done mostly to make things look better and to protect against corrosion.

Electroplating is used in many fields. Jewelry making is one of the most common. Solid gold jewelry is very expensive. In comparison, electroplated gold jewelry is inexpensive. Electroplating permits the look of solid gold without the expense.

Electroplating is also used in producing products like plumbing and electrical fixtures, trophies, medals, cooking utensils, home appliances, automobile parts, and electronic components.

Electroplaters must do very careful work. One reason is that some electroplaters work with rare elements such as gold or silver. Another reason is that some of the electroplating solutions are strong corrosive acids. These include sulfate and cyanide solutions used for plating gold, silver, copper, zinc, nickel, and cadmium. Electroplaters also create plates of alloys such as brass, lead-tin, and bronze.

Experienced electroplaters are always in demand — and the pay is good. Most electroplaters learn their skills as apprentices. Some technical and vocational schools offer courses in electroplating. This is a good idea. There are no educational requirements to become an electroplater. However, high school physics and chemistry will help one understand the theory behind the work. And understanding can lead to better skills, and better pay.

Is electroplating for you?

Give it some thought!

What is corrosion?

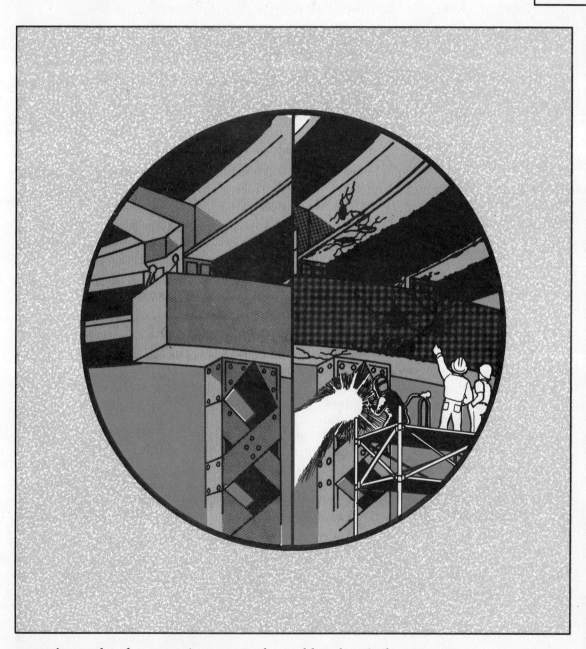

corrosion: the slow wearing away of metal by chemical action
tarnish: a form of corrosion
galvanized: coated with melted zinc

LESSON 23 | What is corrosion?

How often have you seen rust? You don't have to look very far to see it. Just find a car a few years old. Chances are that it has some rust spots.

Car bodies are made of iron. Iron is silver-gray in color. When iron rusts, it turns reddish brown. Rust flakes off easily. Then fresh iron beneath it rusts and flakes away. Little by little, the entire piece of metal rusts away.

Rusting is an example of **corrosion**. Corrosion is the gradual wearing away of metal by chemical action.

The chief cause of corrosion is the oxygen in the air. Other gases that cause corrosion are carbon dioxide, hydrogen sulfide, and water vapor.

Metals like iron, aluminum, and nickel are corroded by oxygen.

The main causes of copper corrosion are carbon dioxide and water vapor. Copper also reacts with hydrogen sulfide. The burning of fuels like coal and natural gas puts hydrogen sulfide into the air. Corrosion changes copper from reddish-orange to green.

Another metal that reacts with hydrogen sulfide is silver. Corroded, or tarnished, silver is black.

The **tarnish** takes away the shiny luster of metal. But sometimes it may be helpful to the life of the metal.

For example, corroded aluminum (aluminum oxide) does not flake off like rust does. It clings to the aluminum and keeps the air away. The corrosion actually forms a protective covering. It stops further corrosion.

Several other metals form protective coats. Copper, zinc, and silver are among them.

Sometimes we may want to prevent corrosion altogether on certain metal objects. This may be done by coating the metal. Such things as paint, lacquer, grease, or even another metal may be used to protect the object against corrosion.

Look at Figures A, B, and C. Then answer the questions with each.

Figure A

Figure A shows silver that has been tarnished. This is the equation for the corrosion of silver.

$$4Ag + 2H_2S \rightarrow 2Ag_2S + 2H_2$$

1. What causes silver to corrode (tarnish)?

   _____

2. What puts this gas into the air?

   _____

3. What is the chemical name for tarnished silver? _____
   (Figure it out from the formula.)

4. Does silver tarnish protect the silver from further corrosion? _____

silver tarnish (Ag_2S)

Figure B

The Statue of Liberty has been standing in New York harbor since 1886.

When it was new, the statue was **reddish-orange** in color. Now it is **green**. Corrosion made it turn color.

5. What metal covers the Statue of Liberty? _____

6. What caused it to corrode? _____

   _____

7. Will the corrosion continue? _____

   _____

8. Why or why not? _____

   _____

   _____

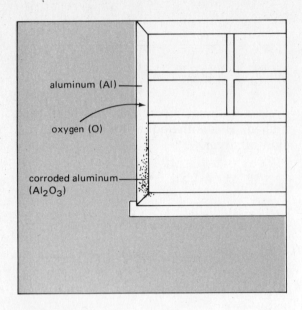

Figure C

Figure C shows corroded aluminum. This is the equation for the corrosion of aluminum:

$$4Al \ + \ 3O_2 \ \rightarrow \ 2Al_2O_3$$
Aluminum oxide

9. What causes aluminum to corrode?

   _____

10. What is the name of the corroded aluminum? _____

11. Does the aluminum oxide protect the aluminum from further corrosion?

    _____

HOW DOES SULFUR AFFECT SILVER?

Background Information

Silver reacts with many sulfur compounds. Egg white contains sulfur.

What You Need (Materials)

hard-boiled egg white
shiny silver spoon

How To Do the Experiment (Procedure)

1. Push the silver spoon into the hard-boiled egg white.

2. Keep it there for about 10 minutes. Then remove it. Compare the part that was inside the egg to the part that was not.

Figure D

What You Saw (Observations)

1. The silver that was in the egg white _____ .
   turned green, turned black, stayed the same

Something To Think About (Conclusions)

1. The silver _____ corrode.
   did, did not

2. What substance corrodes silver? _____

Figure E

Coating metal with paint or lacquer prevents corrosion.

Some protective paint jobs are <u>huge</u>. Take the George Washington Bridge, for example, It takes 25 workers four years and 45,500 liters (12,000 gallons) of paint to cover this structure!

Repainting is done every four to nine years.

Figure F

Figure G

Garbage pails, rain pipes, water pipes, and nails are some **galvanized** products. Galvanizing means dipping metal objects into molten zinc. Galvanizing protects. But it doesn't last forever. It wears off in time.

A tin can is really steel coated with tin.

Coating steel with molten zinc or tin is done by a process called hot-dipping.

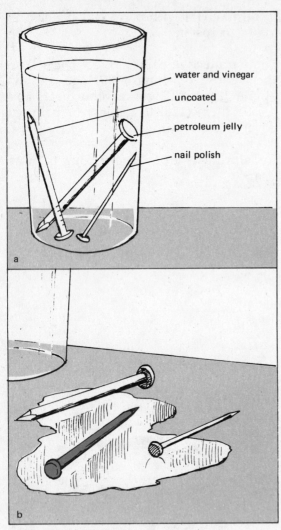

Figure H

Rusting is a form of corrosion that we all know. This is the formula for rusting:

$$4Fe \ + \ 3O_2 \ \rightarrow \ 2Fe_2O_3$$
Iron oxide

Can we prevent iron from rusting?

What You Need To Know (Background Information)

- Iron rusts in water.
- Vinegar, when added to water, speeds the rusting.
- Petroleum jelly is a form of grease.

What You Need (Materials)

3 iron nails
petroleum jelly
clear nail polish
clear water
vinegar
drinking glass

How To Do the Experiment (Procedure)

1. Fill the glass 3/4 full with water. Add a little vinegar and stir.

2. Coat one nail with the clear nail polish. Let it dry.

3. Coat another nail with a thin layer of petroleum jelly

4. Do not coat the third nail.

5. Drop the three nails into the glass. Let them stand overnight. Remove them the next day. Examine each nail.

What You Saw (Observations)

6. The uncoated nail ⎯⎯⎯⎯⎯⎯ rust.
did, did not

7. The coated nails ⎯⎯⎯⎯⎯⎯ rust.
did, did not

Something To Think About (Conclusions)

1. Name two coatings that protect against corrosion. ⎯⎯⎯⎯⎯⎯⎯⎯

2. Name some other ways to protect metal from corrosion. ⎯⎯⎯⎯⎯⎯

FILL IN THE BLANK

Complete each statement using a term or terms from the list below. Write your answers in the spaces provided.

tarnish
oxygen
aluminum oxide
rust
hydrogen sulfide

tin
carbon dioxide
corrosion
iron oxide
prevent

zinc
grease
metal
paint

1. The gradual wearing away of metal by chemical action is called

   _____ .

2. Most corrosion is caused by the _____ in the air.

3. Other gases that cause corrosion are _____ and

   _____ .

4. The most common form of corrosion is _____ .

5. The chemical name for rust is _____ .

6. Sulfur and hydrogen sulfide cause silver to _____ .

7. The chemical name for corroded aluminum is _____ .

8. The corroded aluminum helps _____ further corrosion.

9. We can prevent corrosion by coating metals with _____ ,

   _____ , or even another _____ .

10. Two metals that are used to give a protective coat are _____ and

   _____ .

MATCHING

Match each term in Column A with its description in Column B. Write the correct letter in the space provided.

Column A	Column B
_____ 1. oxygen	a) silver corrosion
_____ 2. rust	b) coated with zinc
_____ 3. tarnish	c) iron oxide
_____ 4. galvanized	d) chief cause of corrosion
_____ 5. corrosion	e) any slow wearing away of metal

TRUE OR FALSE

In the space provided, write "true" if the sentence is true. Write "false" if the sentence is false.

_____ **1.** Corrosion builds metals.

_____ **2.** All metals corrode.

_____ **3.** Most metals corrode.

_____ **4.** Only oxygen causes corrosion.

_____ **5.** Oxygen causes most corrosion.

_____ **6.** Iron can rust.

_____ **7.** Tarnish protects silver from further corrosion.

_____ **8.** Aluminum oxide protects aluminum from further corrosion.

_____ **9.** Carbon dioxide tarnishes silver.

_____ **10.** Zinc and tin tarnish easily.

WORD SCRAMBLE

Below are several scrambled words you have used in this Lesson. Unscramble the words and write your answers in the spaces provided.

1. THRAINS   _____

2. DOORCER   _____

3. LININGAZAGV   _____

4. GOTINCA   _____

5. IMMUNAUL   _____

REACHING OUT

1. You notice a rust spot on a piece of iron. You plan to paint it.

What should you do before you paint the rust spot? _____

Why? _____

_____

2. In what kind of climate does corrosion take place the fastest? _____

_____

What is hard water?

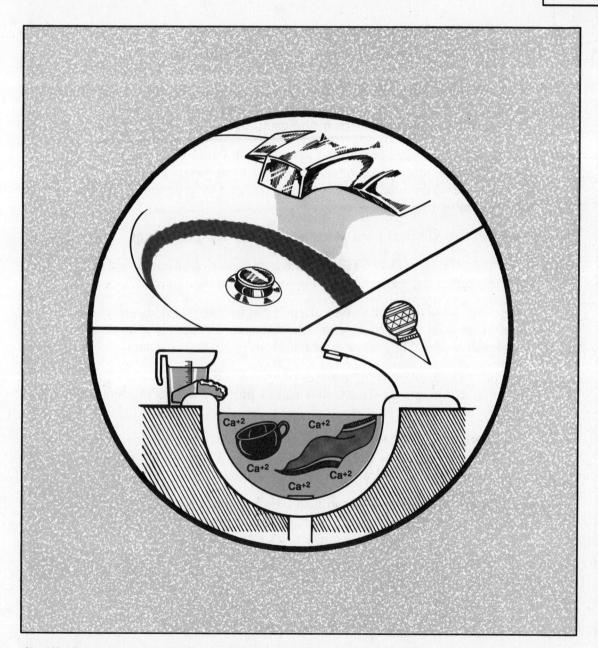

distilled water: pure water with no minerals dissolved in it
hard water: water containing certain dissolved mineral salts; hard water does not lather easily
soft water: water that does not contain the dissolved salts found in hard water; soft water lathers easily

LESSON 24 | What is hard water?

The water you drink is safe but it is not "pure." Pure water has nothing dissolved in it. Tap water has mineral salts dissolved in it. Rainwater picks up these mineral salts from the ground.

There are many kinds of mineral salts. Water that contains dissolved salts of calcium, magnesium, or iron is called **hard water**. Hard water is hard to lather. You need a lot of soap to work up even a small lather. It wastes money, time, and energy.

There are two kinds of hard water—<u>temporary</u> and <u>permanent</u>.

TEMPORARY HARD WATER Temporary hard water contains either calcium bicarbonate, magnesium bicarbonate, or iron bicarbonate.

Temporary hard water can be softened by boiling. Heat decomposes bicarbonate salts. They change to carbonate salts. Carbonate salts do not dissolve in water. They settle to the bottom of their containers.

Another way to soften temporary hard water is by the use of chemical softeners. <u>Washing soda</u>, <u>borax</u>, and <u>slaked</u> <u>lime</u> are common chemical water softeners.

PERMANENT HARD WATER Permanent hard water contains chloride or sulfate salts. It cannot be softened by boiling. Permanent hard water is softened with a chemical softener.

Hard water is a nuisance. It can also be a big problem. The deposit of carbonate salts can clog steam pipes, hot water pipes, and boilers. Also dissolved iron can stain sinks and fabrics. **Soft water** does not cause these problems.

SOFT AND HARD WATER

Study Figures A and B. Then answer the questions.

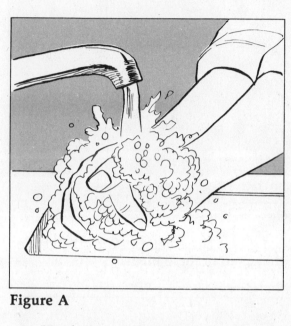

Figure A

Figure B

1. Hard water is being used in Figure _____ .
   _{A, B}

2. Hard water _____ lather easily.
   _{does, does not}

3. Hard water contains dissolved salts of three metals. Name these metals.

   _____ _____ _____

4. Temporary hard water contains dissolved _____ salts.
   _{bicarbonate, chloride or sulfate}

5. Permanent hard water contains dissolved _____ salts.
   _{carbonate, chloride or sulfate}

Place a check mark next to your answer in the next two questions.

6. Temporary hard water can be softened by
   _____ adding a chemical softener
   _____ boiling
   _____ both a and b

7. Permanent hard water can be softened by
   _____ adding a chemical softener
   _____ boiling
   _____ both a and b

8. Name three chemical water softeners. _____ _____

   _____

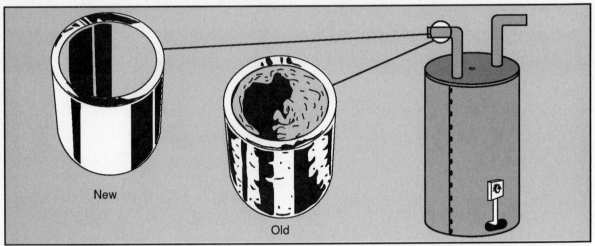

New

Old

Figure C *An example of scale inside a heating pipe.*

Carbonate salts can form deposits on the inside of pipes. These deposits are called scale. Scale cuts the flow of water. In time, what will happen to these pipes?

HARD WATER DETERGENT

Figure D *Soapless detergent*

hard water from water supply

soft water out to house

Figure E *A home water softener*

Some people who live in areas with hard water put water-softening machines in their homes to remove the dissolved salts of calcium, magnesium and iron. Other people in hard-water areas use soapless detergents. Soapless detergents work well in both soft and hard water.

Do you live in a soft-water area or a hard-water area? ——————————————

Water is used in making textiles. Hard water can discolor fabrics.

Fabric manufactures in hard water areas add chemical softeners to their water.

SOFTENING HARD WATER

What You Need (Materials)

four test tubes
liquid soap
washing soda
test tube holder

distilled water
calcium bicarbonate powder
gas burner
test tube rack

How To Do the Experiment (Procedure)

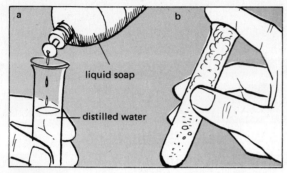

Figure F

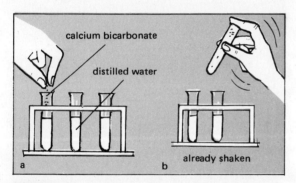

Figure G

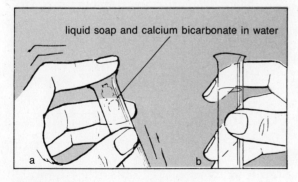

Figure H

Step 1

Half fill a test tube with **distilled water**. Add three drops of liquid soap. Shake.

What You Learned (Observations)

1. The water _____ lather easily.   does, does not

2. Distilled water is _____ water.   hard, soft

3. Distilled water _____   does, does not

   contains dissolved salts.

Step 2

• Half-fill three test tubes with distilled water.
• Add a pinch of calcium bicarbonate to each test tube. Shake.

What You Learned (Observations)

4. The calcium bicarbonate

   _____ dissolve in the   does, does not

   water.

Step 3

Add three drops of liquid soap to one of the test tubes. Shake.

What You Learned (Observations)

5. The water _____ lather easily.   does, does not

6. Water with a dissolved bicarbonate

   salt is _____ water.   hard, soft

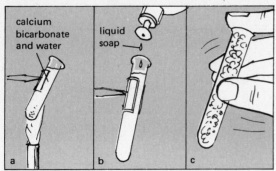

Figure I

What You Learned (Observations)

7. The water now _____ lather easily.

  _{does, does not}

8. The water is now _____ water.

  _{hard, soft}

9. Water with dissolved bicarbonate salt is _____ hard water.

  _{temporary, permanent}

10. Why? _____

The equation below shows how heat changes calcium bicarbonate:

$$Ca(HCO_3)_2 \text{ (dissolved in water)} \xrightarrow{\text{heat}} CaCO_3 + CO_2 + H_2O$$

Calcium bicarbonate — Calcium carbonate — Carbon dioxide — Water

calcium carbonate ($CaCO_3$)
+
water (H_2O)

carbon dioxide (CO_2)

calcium bicarbonate ($CaHCO_3$)

Figure J

11. Boiling changes calcium Bicarbonate to calcium _____ .

12. Calcium bicarbonate _____ dissolve in water.   _{does, does not}

13. What happens to the calcium carbonate? _____

14. The water that forms mixed in with the rest of the water. What happens to the carbon dioxide? _____

washing soda.

liquid soap

hard water

Figure K

Step 4

- Boil the mixture in the second test tube. (Remember, It contains hard water.) Allow it to cool.

- Add three drops of liquid soap. Shake.

Step 5

- Sprinkle some washing soda into the third test tube. (Remember, it contains hard water.) Shake. Let it stand for a minute.

- Add three drops of liquid soap. Shake.

What You Learned (Observations)

15. The water _____ lather easily.
    does, does not

16. The water is now _____ water.
    hard, soft

17. What changed the hard water to soft water? _____

18. Washing soda "softens" hard water. Name two other water softeners.

    _____ _____

Something To Think About (Conclusions)

1. Water softeners can soften temporary hard water. Can water softeners soften permanent hard water? _____

2. Temporary hard water can be softened by boiling. Can permanent hard water be softened by boiling? _____

3. Temporary hard water contains _____ salts.
   bicarbonate, chloride or sulfate

4. Permanent hard water contains _____ salts.
   bicarbonate, chloride or sulfate

5. Name the three metals (elements) found in hard water. _____

   _____ _____

MINERAL SALTS AND HARD WATER

Six salts are listed below. Fill in the spaces next to each salt with the correct information. The first line has been done for you.

Salt	Produces temporary hard water or permanent hard water	Water softened by boiling	Water softened with a water softener
1. Magnesium sulfate		no	yes
2. Calcium chloride			
3. Magnesium bicarbonate			
4. Iron sulfate			
5. Calcium bicarbonate			
6. Iron chloride			

FILL IN THE BLANK

Complete each statement using a term or terms from the list below. Write your answers in the spaces provided. Some words may be used more than once.

ground	hard water	chemical softener
borax	salts	temporary
permanent	boiling	hot water pipes
slaked lime	scale	sulfate
chloride	bicarbonate	washing soda

1. Tap water has mineral _____ dissolved in it.

2. Rainwater picks up mineral salts from the _____ .

3. Water that contains calcium, magnesium, or iron salts is called_____ .

4. There are two kinds of hard water. They are _____ and _____ hard water.

5. Temporary hard water contains _____ salts.

6. Permanent hard water contains_____ or _____ salts.

7. Temporary hard water can be softened by _____ or by adding a

   _____ .

8. Permanent hard water cannot be softened by_____ .

9. Three chemical water softeners are _____ , _____ , and

   _____ .

10. Carbonate deposits are called _____ . These deposits can clog

   _____ .

WORD SCRAMBLE

Below are several scrambled words you have used in this Lesson. Unscramble the words and write your answers in the spaces provided.

1. RABBITCANOE   _____

2. SODELSIDV   _____

3. LASEC   _____

4. LIDDLESTI   _____

5. RAMINEL   _____

How are metals important to life and health?

25

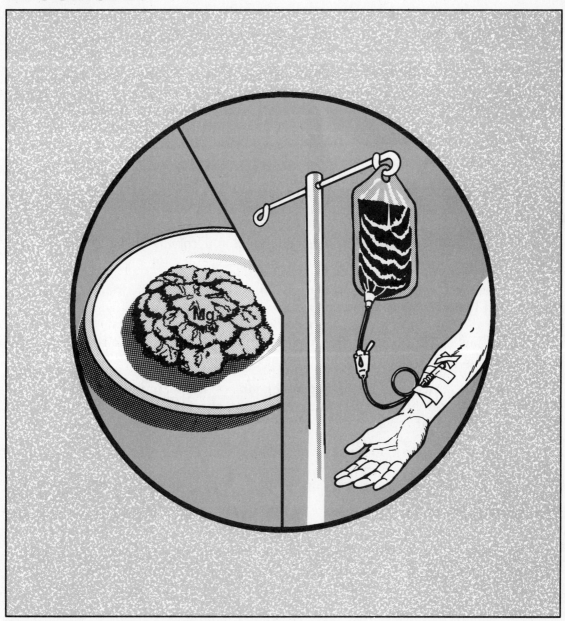

chlorophyll: important compound that contains magnesium, found in green plants
hemoglobin: important compound that contains iron, found in blood
trace amounts: extremely small amounts

LESSON 25 | How are metals important to life and health?

There can be no life without metals. They are part of all living things, including you. There is metal in your blood, for example. Your red blood cells contain an iron compound called **hemoglobin** [He-muh-glow-bin]. Hemoglobin picks up oxygen and carries it to all parts of your body. Your blood also contains sodium (the metal in table salt), which helps control the balance between water and salt in your body.

Your body needs the metal calcium for bones, teeth, blood clotting, and muscle movement. Both sodium and potassium are needed for proper functioning of your nerves. Your body also has **trace amounts** of other metals such as magnesium, copper, zinc, and cobalt. These trace elements help the body carry out functions necessary for life.

Where do these metals come from? You get them from the food you eat and the water you drink. How do metals get into food and water? The metals come from the rocks and soil. Water dissolves minerals containing metals, and plants take up these minerals through their roots. We eat the plants, or the animals that have eaten the plants.

Soil on farms can lose its supply of minerals with important metals. Minerals can get used up after years of planting. So farmers often use fertilizers that replace metals in the soil.

Metals also help in everyday health care. Metals are in products such as toothpaste, soap, talcum powder, milk of magnesia, mercurochrome, calamine lotion, and epsom salts. How many of these products have you used?

ONE METAL NECESSARY FOR ALL LIFE

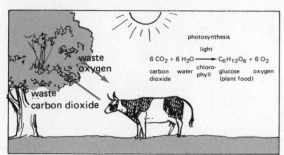

Figure A *This shows how plants make oxygen and food.*

Without <u>magnesium</u>, there might not be life as we know it. Why? Plants make their own food from carbon dioxide and water. They use the energy from sunlight to help build food molecules. A plant compound called **chlorophyll** [KLOR-uh-fill] traps the sun's energy. This process is called <u>photosynthesis</u>. See Figure A.

The formula for chlorophyll is $C_{55}H_{72}O_5N_4Mg$.

1. One molecule of chlorophyll contains 137 atoms. How many of these atoms come

   from the metal magnesium? _____

2. Can photosynthesis take place without chlorophyll? _____

3. **a)** Why is magnesium important to plants? _____

   _____

   b) Why is magnesium important to people? _____

   _____

A plant takes in magnesium through its roots. It takes in other minerals, too. The minerals include potassium, zinc, iron, copper, and boron.

A balanced diet contains all the minerals a person needs.

Figure B

4. Where do minerals come from? _____

5. Which life form takes in minerals first—plants or animals? _____

6. How do people get their minerals? _____

   _____

7. What can happen to soil on farms? _____

8. What do farmers add to soil to replace minerals? _____

Figure C

Fertilizers can increase crop size. They can also make poor soil into soil that is good for farming.

9. Why are fertilizers becoming more

and more important?_____

_____

_____

Did you ever add "plant food" to the soil of your house plants?

10. Plant "food" isn't really "food." What

does it contain?_____

_____

_____

FILL IN THE BLANK

Complete each statement using a term or terms from the list below. Write your answers in the spaces provided. Some words may be used more than once.

sodium	soil	iron
photosynthesis	magnesium	plants
blood	animals	oxygen
calcium		

1. Plants take in metals from the _____.

2. We get our minerals (metals) by eating _____ or _____ that have eaten plants.

3. The metal in common table salt is _____ .

4. Dissolved sodium is an important part of _____ .

5. Hemoglobin contains the metal _____ .

6. Hemoglobin picks up and delivers _____ to the body.

7. The metal that helps build strong bones and teeth is _____ .

8. Chlorophyll contains the metal _____ .

9. Chlorophyll is needed for food-making in plants. This is called _____ .

10. Plants give us food and _____ .

THE METRIC SYSTEM

METRIC-ENGLISH CONVERSIONS

	Metric to English	English to Metric
Length	1 kilometer = 0.621 mile (mi)	1 mi = 1.61 km
	1 meter = 3.28 feet (ft)	1 ft = 0.305 m
	1 centimeter = 0.394 inch (in)	1 in = 2.54 cm
Area	1 square meter = 10.763 square feet	1 ft^2 = 0.0929 m^2
	1 square centimeter = 0.155 square inch	1 in^2 = 6.452 cm^2
Volume	1 cubic meter = 35.315 cubic feet	1 ft^3 = 0.0283 m^3
	1 cubic centimeter = 0.0610 cubic inches	1 in^3 = 16.39 cm^3
	1 liter = .2642 gallon (gal)	1 gal = 3.79 L
	1 liter = 1.06 quart (qt)	1 qt = 0.94 L
Mass	1 kilogram = 2.205 pound (lb)	1 lb = 0.4536 kg
	1 gram = 0.0353 ounce (oz)	1 oz = 28.35 g
Temperature	Celsius = 5/9 (°F −32)	Fahrenheit = 9/5°C + 32
	0°C = 32°F (Freezing point of water)	72°F = 22°C (Room temperature)
	100°C = 212°F	98.6°F = 37°C
	(Boiling point of water)	(Human body temperature)

METRIC UNITS

The basic unit is printed in capital letters.

Length	Symbol
Kilometer	km
METER	m
centimeter	cm
millimeter	mm

Area	Symbol
square kilometer	km^2
SQUARE METER	m^2
square millimeter	mm^2

Volume	Symbol
CUBIC METER	m^3
cubic millimeter	mm^3
liter	L
milliliter	mL

Mass	Symbol
KILOGRAM	kg
gram	g

Temperature	Symbol
degree Celsius	°C

SOME COMMON METRIC PREFIXES

Prefix		Meaning
micro-	=	0.000001, or 1/1,000,000
milli-	=	0.001, or 1/1000
centi-	=	0.01, or 1/100
deci-	=	0.1, or 1/10
deka-	=	10
hecto-	=	100
kilo-	=	1000
mega-	=	1,000,000

SOME METRIC RELATIONSHIPS

Unit	Relationship
kilometer	1 km = 1000 m
meter	1 m = 100 cm
centimeter	1 cm = 10 mm
millimeter	1 mm = 0.1 cm
liter	1 L = 1000 mL
milliliter	1 mL = 0.001 L
tonne	1 t = 1000 kg
kilogram	1 kg = 1000 g
gram	1 g = 1000 mg
centigram	1 cg = 10 mg
milligram	1 mg = 0.001 g

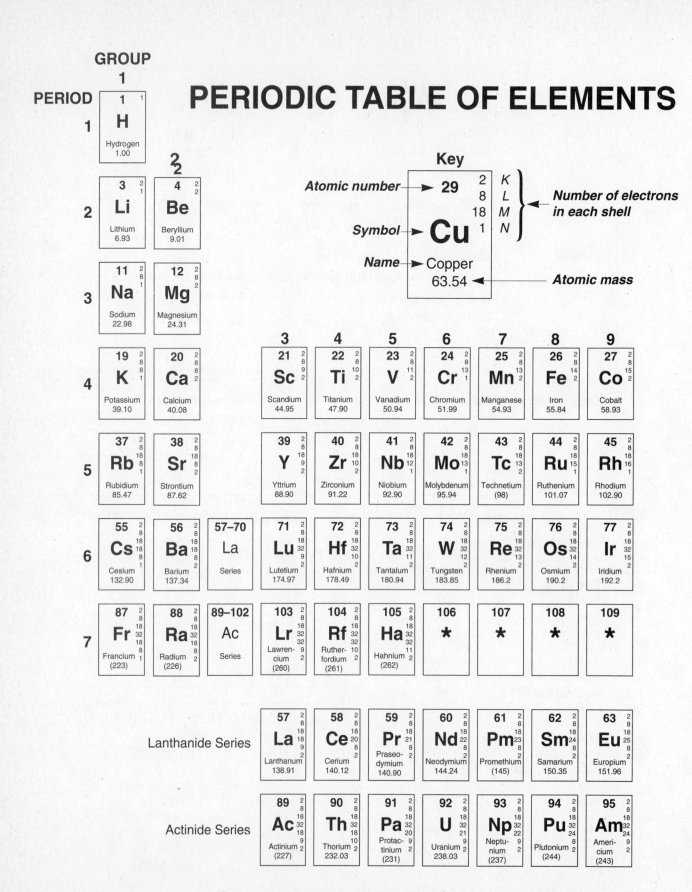

PERIODIC TABLE OF ELEMENTS

GROUP

PERIOD

Key

Atomic number → 29 — 2, 8, 18, 1 — K L M N — Number of electrons in each shell

Symbol → **Cu**

Name → Copper

63.54 ← Atomic mass

Lanthanide Series

Actinide Series

* Names for these elements have not been agreed upon.

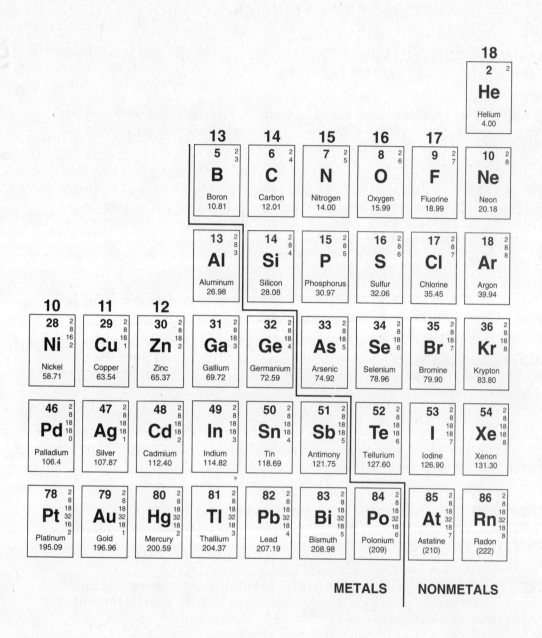

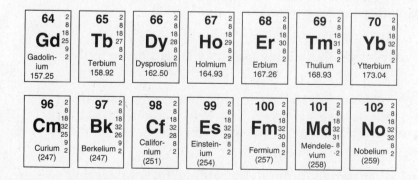

SAFETY ALERT SYMBOLS

 CLOTHING PROTECTION • A lab coat protects clothing from stains. • Always confine loose clothing.

 EYE SAFETY • Always wear safety goggles. • If anything gets in your eyes, flush them with plenty of water. • Be sure you know how to use the emergency wash system in the laboratory.

 FIRE SAFETY • Never get closer to an open flame than is necessary. • Never reach across an open flame. • Confine loose clothing. • Tie back loose hair. • Know the location of the fire-extinguisher and fire blanket. • Turn off gas valves when not in use. • Use proper procedures when lighting any burner.

 POISON • Never touch, taste, or smell any unknown substance. Wait for your teacher's instruction.

 CAUSTIC SUBSTANCES • Some chemicals can irritate and burn the skin. If a chemical spills on your skin, flush it with plenty of water. Notify your teacher without delay.

 HEATING SAFETY • Handle hot objects with tongs or insulated gloves. • Put hot objects on a special lab surface or on a heat-resistant pad; never directly on a desk or table top.

 SHARP OBJECTS • Handle sharp objects carefully. • Never point a sharp object at yourself, or anyone else. • Cut in the direction away from your body.

 TOXIC VAPORS • Some vapors (gases) can injure the skin, eyes, and lungs. Never inhale vapors directly. • Use your hand to "wave" a small amount of vapor towards your nose.

 GLASSWARE SAFETY • Never use broken or chipped glassware. • Never pick up broken glass with your bare hands.

 CLEAN UP • Wash your hands thoroughly after any laboratory activity.

 ELECTRICAL SAFETY • Never use an electrical appliance near water or on a wet surface. • Do not use wires if the wire covering seems worn. • Never handle electrical equipment with wet hands.

 DISPOSAL • Discard all materials properly according to your teacher's directions.

GLOSSARY/INDEX

alloy: a blend of metals, 126
atoms: the smallest parts of an element that have all the properties of that element, 2

balanced equation: description of a reaction that obeys the Law of Conservation of Matter so that the kind and number of atoms on both sides of the equation is equal, 72

chemical change: change in matter that produces new products, 66
chemical equation: set of symbols and formulas that describe a chemical change, 66
chlorophyll [KLOWR-uh-fil]: important compound that contains magnesium, found in green plants, 163
coefficient [koh-uh-FISH-unt]: number that shows how many molecules of a substance are involved in a chemical reaction, 63
coke: a form of carbon that reacts with oxide ores, 119
compound: matter made up of two or more elements that are linked together, 2
corrosion: the slow wearing away of metal by chemical action, 146

decomposition [dee-kahm-puh-ZISH-un]: breakdown of a substance into simpler substances, 92
distilled water: pure water with no minerals dissolved in it, 157
ductile: able to be drawn into thin wire, 38

electrolysis [i-lek-TRAHL-uh-sis]: decomposition of a substance by means of electricity, 92
electron: a part of the atom that moves around the nucleus; an electron has a negative electrical charge, 8
electroplating: putting a coating on a metal by using electricity, 132
element: matter that is made up of only one kind of atom, 2

formula mass: sum of the mass numbers of all the atoms in a molecule, 60

galvanized: coated with melted zinc, 149

hard water: water containing certain dissolved mineral salts; hard water does not lather easily, 154
hemoglobin [HEE-muh-gloh-bin]: important compound that contains iron, found in blood, 162

ion [Y-on]: an atom with a charge, 33

Law of Conservation of Matter: scientific statement that says that a chemical reaction does not destroy or create matter, 78

malleable: able to be thinned out by rolling or hammering without breaking apart, 38
mass: a measure of the amount of matter, 2
matter: anything that has mass and volume, 2
metal activity: the ease with which metals react with other elements to form positive metal ions, 140
metallurgist: a scientist who studies metals, 112
metallurgy [MET-uh-lur-jee]: the science of separating metals from the ores in which they are found, 112
mineral: a solid substance found in the earth's crust, 112

neutron: a part of the atom found inside the nucleus; a neutron has no electrical charge, 8
nucleus: the center part of an atom, 8

ore: a mineral that contains a useful amount of metal, 112
oxidation [ahk-suh-DAY-shun]: linkup of oxygen with another substance; a loss of electrons, 104
oxidation number: how many electrons an atom can lend or borrow, 44

periodic table: a chart of the elements, 14
physical change: change in matter that does not produce any new products, 66

polyatomic [PAHL-i-uh-tahm-ik] **ion:** group of atoms that acts as a single atom, 52

polyvalent [pahl-i-VAY-lunt]: having more than one oxidation number, 56

product: a substance that is produced in a chemical reaction (change), 66

properties: anything about matter that helps identify it, 14

proton: a part of the atom found inside the nucleus; a proton has a positive electrical charge, 8

reactant: substance that takes part in a chemical reaction (change), 66

reducing agent: a material that takes the oxygen out of an ore, 118

reduction [ri-DUK-shun]: separation of oxygen from a substance; a gain of electrons, 104

replacement reaction: reaction in which one kind of matter replaces another kind, 98

roasting: heating an ore in the open air, 118

shell: a level outside the nucleus in which electrons move, 22

soft water: water that does not contain the dissolved salts found in hard water; soft water lathers easily, 154

subscript: number written to the lower right of a chemical symbol, 52

synthesis [SIN-thuh-sis] **reaction:** combining of several substances to form a more complicated substance, 86

tarnish: a form of corrosion, 146

trace amounts: extremely small amounts, 162

unbalanced equation: description of a reaction that does not obey the Law of Conservation of Matter, 72

volume: the amount of space that matter takes up, 2